THE MAN
OF THE FAMILY

THE MAN OF THE FAMILY

Robert Wallace Bennett

Homestead Lighthouse Press

Grants Pass, Oregon

Names: Bennett, Robert Wallace-author.

Library of Congress Control Number: 2022948846
ISBN 978-1-950475-27-8
Homestead Lighthouse Press
1668 NE Foothill Boulevard
Unit A
Grants Pass, OR 97526
www.homesteadlighthousepress.com

Distributed by Homestead Lighthouse Press, Daedalus Distribution, Amazon.com, Barnes & Noble

Cover & Book Design: Ray Rhamey, Ashland, OR
Cover photo by the author—of the author

Homestead Lighthouse Press gratefully acknowledges the generous support of its readers and patrons.

For Alice, without whom this story would not exist, and for Robert, John and Alyssa, without whom it would be only half as good.

Prologue

Here he stands on the sidewalk, savoring a crisp but sunny morning at the start of September, the Vermont maple foliage still mostly forest green but rimmed with red. Then he bounds up the brick steps to the Doric columns and the door of Woodruff Hall, the administration building, raring to register for classes. The building certainly belongs on a New England college campus, with its marble pillars and pediments, statues and bronze plaques and all the ivy-covered walls any college wannabe could crave.

He sizes up the surroundings, one hundred percent collegiate. He took a long road to get here, not so much in miles but in time. He sighs and smiles when he reaches the door. It's journey's end.

Fresh out of the Air Force, he recalls the final question by his officer in charge, Captain Ray Porfilio, a native New Yorker, just a few days before his discharge.

"What are your plans?"

"I'm going to college."

"Excellent. A lot of civilians can sail through this life very successfully without ever going to college. But you? You *need* college!"

The captain's only kidding, but cognizant. He does need college. He yearned it years earlier but went without. With a college degree, he might have been the commissioned officer doing the chiding, not the enlisted man receiving the ribbing.

That was only a couple of weeks ago. Six years in the future he will poke fun at Porfilio when he meets him as an equal. Both will be civilian public relations managers in New York.

It took five long years to get into college, from 1954 until '59. Long? Menial jobs for a year and then languish four in the service. It's like a sentence. Oh yeah, three major schools of journalism accepted him back in '54—Syracuse, Seton Hall and Marquette, his only choices.

Rejection didn't keep him out.

Money did. The lack thereof.

Forget getting any dough from his divorced father. His similarly split mother's father reneges on a promise to pay when he remarries, to a Canadian woman. She insists gramp's assets should be in her bank account. And his Godfather, a self-made man of means who mastered no more than seventh grade, never fails to pronounce to everyone who will listen that college produces only educated fools. No sense asking him. A veteran of World War I, he says join the army because "It will make a man out of you."

Bob replies he's already one, reminding him that when his father went into World War II, he became the "man of the family."

So, after the Air Force, he accepts this state college, one he can afford, near a newspaper with a reporting position that will provide sufficient funds to support him. He can commute from his mother's home twelve miles away. Is commuting a bad thing? Who desires four years in a dormitory after four on a bunk in a barracks? After military regulations, with reeking mess halls and tin trays, discussions of dames, discipline and stupidity and dissecting the world's disasters, he absolutely prefers his mother's cooking and his own bed.

Now he stands on the top step, enjoying the satisfaction of attaining his goal. It's as if he blasted a walk-off grand slam in the bottom of the ninth in the seventh game against the Yankees.

But wait. It's really only a marathon starting line. Will he take it all the way to the tape? Five long years have passed since he sat in a classroom. He studied very little then. Can he cut it now?

The picturesque school in Vermont offers few majors, but so what, he can pick only one. He selects English. He always aced it and already has read most of the books he will be assigned.

Once inside the administration building he senses instantly that *she* makes the place more than merely picturesque. As her high heels click down the marble-tiled hall, a belted and buttoned cotton shirt-waist halts abruptly over amazing ankles. Just below the hem it is ankles away.

He stops abruptly. He stares.

He's enchanted. She swishes demurely, blonde tresses swinging this way and that; smiling and melting everyone she meets. It's lots more than ankles—all the probably hundred and five pounds of anatomy are exactly where any guy would wish they were. She is so pretty she races his pulse; the features of her face and all the rest of her remind him of a porcelain figurine. Maybe even a statue if it is five feet four.

A staffer, not a student, she is the bursar, accounting big shot, boss of the budget, princess of the payables and the power behind the president.

Hello Miss Charming and Dependable!

Is it love at first sight?

Impossible.

He has seen her many times before.

Part One: Before

Chapter One

Smitten

The first week of the semester the seniors follow a silly tradition. They demand freshmen don ridiculous little round caps.

Beanies.

A newly minted senior, much delighted to be one, overtakes him on the sidewalk between classes.

"You're a freshman, right?

"Right."

"Where's your beanie?"

"I haven't got one."

"Better get one or I'll report you."

"I'm not wearing one so report me if you like."

"You'll have to go to student court."

"I won't go. I don't have time for that. I've got a job and I have to go to work."

"Then they'll sentence you in absentia."

"Whatever it is, I won't be doing it."

After three years, nine months and twenty-seven days compelled to wear an overseas cap and one with a visor and a contrived sixty-mission crush he is completely opposed to conforming. Anyone caught bare headed by an ape, an Air Force policeman, receives a discrepancy report and assigned extra duty, such as latrine cleaning. It also blemishes your personnel record, which could ruin your chance of promotion. So any dopey senior who thinks he'll wear a beanie is dreaming.

The next day a note appears in his mailbox. The court sentence: two weeks mopping the dining hall, starting tomorrow. He wads it up and whips it toward the wastebasket. He mopped his last mess or dining hall on KP.

His *very* last. Never again.

Two days later he finds a summons form in his box from the dean of students. So he goes to see him and *she* is also in his office, having told the dean she remembers him from high school. Turns out the dean, an Air Force vet, loves trout fishing. He pulls out a couple of Cuban cigars, they light up and swap service stories while she coughs and turns up her nose. He then hands Bob a box of trout flies he tied, matched for the hatch at the nearby river.

Somebody else must have mopped the dining room floor.

The next day the doll's in the library at lunchtime. And the next. And the next, because they must review the last five years. She has been graduated from business college, held a management job at a mountain resort. The librarian, ordinarily affable, now annoyed, will toss out other chattering twosomes, but simply arches an eyebrow. One recipient of her glare is a mere student, a freshman no less, but she is Miss Charming and Dependable. Not to mention the princess of the payroll.

Who writes the librarian's paycheck.

Most days these meetings consume his complete lunchtime. On others he takes her down the road to the Birdseye Diner. Actually, she drives him in her dad's big Oldsmobile Ninety-eight. Afterward, he rides to his job as a reporter at the daily paper a dozen miles away, with another commuting student, Rita Morgan. Rita, fifteen years his senior, is a friend of his mother. A widowed mother of five, she will graduate two years ahead of him and mentor his first stint as a student teacher.

He does of course remember Miss C&D from high school, but neither had paid any attention to the other then. A year ahead of him, like other older girls she had nothing to do with supposedly immature younger boys. Boys knew they had no chance with an older girl. Most important, her mother wouldn't let her out on dates with anyone. He remembers nothing about her ankles. Bobby sox and saddle shoes prevented that. So did parochial school jumpers and starched white blouses, no match for clicking heels and a shirt-waist. But knowing they had both been there gives them a certain comfort level. Five years later their single year age difference seems insignificant.

He is smitten, no doubt. He can tell she is too. Where will it go from here? Much doubt. Here he is with little money, college expenses, no car, and a future that seems a long way from now. Where is she? Big bucks, twenty-four years old, ready for marriage, her future here and now.

Yeah, plenty of doubt.

At the same time, he can't conceal a degree of confidence. He's older than all the other students. He has served his country, gone halfway around the globe, been shot at, survived a plane crash, interviewed world figures and written for pay. So he thinks his experience and age give him an edge on the competition. He's even a bit smug.

He knows he will win her approval.

Maybe.

Chapter Two

Rejection

Earlier he named another blonde the Breck Girl because of the magazine shampoo ads that showcased pretty girls with golden strands falling to their shoulders. He spotted her on his way up Grove Street in Rutland to fish at Patch Pond. Ten years old, she sat with a book on a marble bench at a goldfish pond by the grand Vaughan mansion, the biggest house in town, one in imposing shingle style with a great gambrel roof and a gorgeous view of Pico and Killington peaks to the east.

Eight years later she is pretty in a pink dress over her summer tan. He loves the way her strappy white shoes click on the sidewalk as they march down Grove Street to the Paramount for a movie. His feet barely touch the ground.

A devout Catholic, she attends Mass with her mother every morning. Eighteen now, she remains quite innocent, even naïve. That trait strikes him the night they take in the play *Stalag 17* at the high school auditorium, performed by a touring company. The "animal" stands over the footlights, staring down at Shapiro taking a bath in a washtub.

"Shapiro," he says, "I didn't know you was Jewish."

That elicits a lot of laughs from most of the audience.

But not from the Breck Girl.

"What's so funny? she whispers.

"I'll tell you later,"

But he never does.

Two years later it finally dawns on her that a boyfriend two thousand miles away with no money and no car and no apparent prospects is no fun. The ultimate rejection arrives in a "Dear John" letter at the Francis E. Warren air base in Cheyenne. Absence makes the heart grow colder. Three years later she will marry a salaried automobile tire salesman.

That letter contained the best message of rejection he had ever received, although he didn't realize it of course. Recalling it now makes him uneasy. Rejection once again seems a strong possibility.

Quite.

Will he win and keep Miss Charming? Can he string her along while still a student? Or will she be another Breck Girl? He does hold a full-time job, but only at the minimum wage, a dollar an hour. While grateful for it, he gripes about it too. As a senior in high school the same publisher paid him the minimum wage to cover local sports. It was seventy-five cents then.

In the past five years he edited the paper for all of the Air Force in Korea and two other newspapers stateside. His stories appeared in the worldwide *Air Force Times.* He sold stories to *Military Market,* a trade magazine for post and base exchanges and commissaries. He wrote simultaneously for civilian newspapers in two states for more than he made in the military. He produced articles and photo features as a resident staff writer for *Stars & Stripes* in Tokyo. He wrote two volumes of the history of a fifteen-hundred bed hospital, the biggest in the Air Force.

And all that experience amounted to twenty-five cents more than he made five years before.

What's more, the job was offered for a mere six months while another reporter served an obligatory term in the army (although the guy never returned to reclaim his position).

And still, it remains an absolute joy to retain the job. He needs it, sure, but loves it. In time he will earn more, get promoted and earn still more. He will handle every position in the newsroom, supervise everyone in it and even direct promotional sections with the ad department. In the next five years, extracting more money from his publisher will be a big challenge, but his newspaper salary will more than quadruple.

On the way to that, when he receives a five-dollar a week raise he asks for five more. And get this, publisher Bob Mitchell says you deserve it but he can't give it to you because "You started out too low." Meanwhile, the college president nominates him for listing in *Who's Who in the East* and *Outstanding Young Men of America*. He also lands on another sucker list as one of *Ten Thousand Young Men of Achievement*.

But will he win Miss C&D?

Only time will tell.

Chapter Three

Conquering Classrooms

At the moment, however, a buck an hour doesn't go very far. The fact is, though, if he could afford to, he will toil here for nothing. But he chips in board and room for his mother. He must pay the state tax department five hundred dollars. That's a hot one. Turns out the Air Force never deducted Vermont taxes from his pay checks over the four years. He never thought about them because he served his country elsewhere all that time, including more than a year outside of it, in Asia. Federal taxes produced his paycheck and he paid them. Talk about government double dipping. Some states gave vets mustering out bonuses of about five hundred bucks. Vermont paid nothing; instead wanted that much.

"What if I don't pay it?" he asks the state tax guy.

"Well, you can claim you were not a resident, but if you do you will have to come up with the non-resident tuition rate at the state college."

That's more than the five hundred so he pays it off a month at a time out of his buck an hour. Then a funny thing happens about the tuition. He doesn't have to pay that after all. All these years he was concerned he couldn't afford tuition. Now he doesn't need to pay any even with enough money in his pocket.

Okay, barely enough.

He would never guess why.

After five years in journalism, he aces an English composition test required of all incoming frosh. He gets excused from the otherwise required first year comp course. He thinks he could teach it. To fill the gap in his planned eighteen-credit schedule, he signs up for a senior American lit course. The imperious, stuffed shirt prof, head of the English department, suffers some kind of an affront for a freshman to take it and regards him with disdain.

When Bob produces a term paper about Captain John Smith in pulp paperback style it returns with a note that he certainly plagiarized it. Furthermore, it bellows with braggadocio as the perfectly typewritten product of a Royal standard on white bond while classmates' submissions come scribbled in cursive on lined notebook filler. Not to mention the active voice, perfect grammar, spelling and syntax.

The term paper carries half the grade for the course. It is accorded an *F.*

Despite "A" marks on tests and exams, which alone would be worth a passing "C" for the course, he flunks. The prof says plagiarism is the reason.

His city editor writes a note attesting to Bob having typed the paper in front of him after working hours. It carries no weight. It helps not when the editor adds that while he knows the work to be original, he thinks it's hardly worthy of the charge of plagiarism. Adding that it's really not very good he thus insults the prof.

Darned if the city editor and the prof hadn't been classmates at Harvard and despised each other ever since, one for merely teaching at a small college and the other for only editing a small-town daily. Never mind that the editor had already been a reporter at the big-time Boston daily, *P.M.*

Bob appeals the grade to the college president after Miss Charming tells him of Bob's accomplishments as a professional writer.

"Look at it from my position," the president says. "I agree this is unjust, but I have to support faculty decisions."

While he loses the three credits, the president hires him to write news releases about the college construction program and to advise the student newspaper and gives him a free ride on the tuition. So now he's the college publicist and "faculty" adviser to the student newspaper while a still a freshman—sans beanie.

And wonder of wonders, he doesn't have to pay the tuition he always worried he couldn't.

He takes the class again the next semester, from the same prof, handing in a sheet of typed bond that bears only the words, "I have already fulfilled the term paper requirement for this course."

He finds it back in his mailbox the next day, adorned with an "A."

It's followed by "A" for the course. The word, or words, has gotten around.

The experience teaches him that because a final exam is worth half the final grade and the term paper the other half, he can quickly and easily knock out a paper with an "A," then even so much as flunk a final and still wind up with at least a passing "C." So that's his plan for the rest of his college career. He simply grabs the first books he finds on a pertinent subject, flips through them for salient points and produces a term paper with a preconceived conclusion out of what presents itself. In fact, by signing up for both history and lit courses of the same era in the same semester he can make two copies, slap a separate cover sheet on each, and pull in two "A's." Lit profs love it when he injects a little period background info, and vice-versa for the history instructors.

With accurate typing, perfect spelling and grammar and punctuation plus a heap of hyperbole amid a putrid compost heap of classmates' hen-scratched papers, the faculty enthusiastically find it refreshing.

The "*A*" grades pile up.

He makes the dean's list.

The student who longed to get into college now knows what he really wants—to get out, keep writing and making more money. Inside the ivy-covered buildings he learns what he considers his most important collegiate lesson: there is a whole lot to know and nobody else knows much of it either. That realization confers a degree of self-confidence greater than any diploma can.

For certain, the ivy-covered walls wipe out the despair he suffered as a stock boy and enlisted man while high school classmates went to college and got commissions.

Chapter Four
Getting Started

As a five-year old in Cranford, New Jersey, Bobby already reads with curiosity. He learns how with help from the New York radio station WOR. Every Sunday morning Uncle Don asks all the little kiddies to lay the *New York Journal-American* comic pages on the living room floor. Bobby kneels on the thick wool carpet beneath the 1941 Zenith floor model console radio, with its wood veneer cabinet impersonating fine furniture, and sings with Don the opening song:

"Hello nephews, nieces too, mothers and daddies how are you! This is Uncle Don, set to go, with a meeting on the radio."

Bobby follows all the funnies—his favorites include The Katzenjammer Kids, Li'l Abner and Prince Valiant—as Uncle Don reads to him.

Yes, that's the same Uncle Don whose popular weekly program will be permanently mute after he thinks his microphone is dead at the end of one such episode and says:

"Well, that ought to hold the little bastards for another week."

Bobby's mother reads voraciously. Before her marriage she worked and read in the Newark Public Library. She buys her son *Big Little Books, Little Golden Books* and comics. By first grade he has been reading on his own for over a year. He suffers when others stutter and struggle with Dick and Jane and Spot and Puff, excruciatingly pausing seemingly forever to sound out syllables. Even a long, new piece of chalk screeching on the blackboard, sending shivers down his back, sounds better.

He also loves to draw, mostly cars and airplanes. His mother, certain he is talented, becomes a willing patron, buying him paint sets and big boxes of crayons. By fifth grade, living in San Francisco, he submits drawings of baseball players, some copied from Wheaties cereal boxes to the Oakland Tribune Aunt Elsie's children's page. He wins pencil box prizes.

The real payoff, however, comes seeing his work in print, which leads to a passion for writing stories. In seventh grade he writes a gossipy, one-page, one-copy newspaper called the *Gopher Boy Gazette* which he passes around the classroom until it's nipped by the nun. What really gets him going into journalism, however, is being pals with a boy named Gerry whose father is the managing editor of the morning newspaper for which he will one day work.

Bob and Gerry often hang out in the newsroom after school. Gerry's dad gives them little writing assignments, which include items about Cub and Boy Scouts, 4-H clubs and recreation department activities. Those organizations submit hand-written reports that require sharpening into stories, succinctly, without redundancy and repetition and mistakes in spelling. The two boys try to revise them and manage to peck out sentences on the manual Royal and Underwood typewriters while the city desk reporters are out covering their beats. They hand them in to Gerry's dad, who smiles approvingly and then delivers them to his day editor. She rewrites them the way they should have been in the first place (and the second) and gives the boys a few pointers. Bob and Gerry find their few paragraphs in the next day's paper and think them marvelous.

Gerry' family soon moves away when his father is fired for drinking on the job too often. It's a lucky break for Bob. A few years later when it's time to choose the next high school sports reporter Bob gets the job Gerry assuredly would have won. It's an ill boozy breath that doesn't blow somebody some good, but years later Gerry achieves great success. He goes on after college to report for the *Providence Journal* and then becomes press secretary to presidential hopeful and New York governor Nelson Rockefeller.

With his paid sports writing experience, classmates vote Bob editor of the high school paper, but the adviser nun soon fires him because he fails to provide any leadership, or even any articles. His head swells; he thinks he's too big time to fool around with the high school rag. It's one rejection he doesn't mind at all.

Two years later, his reporting on the daily gives Bob hope for a letter of recommendation for an Air Force journalism job. While he's in basic training, an envelope arrives at the air base from his former sports editor, now the managing editor. He is the gruff Willard P. (Bill) Dexter Jr., whose many long nights in a swivel chair taught him to balance a beer belly on both knees. Bob excitedly rips it open.

His jaw drops.

"You've got one helluva nerve asking me for a recommendation. You can't spell worth a gawdam and Tippy Pliska had to finish typing your copy or you never would have made the sports deadline."

But inside, in another letter, he finds a glowing recommendation. That, plus clippings his mother mails, clinch the position of historian at the third largest military hospital in the world, complete with the Air Force Specialty Code and designation as an information specialist—which is the career field of journalism.

Chapter Five
Pre-war Idyll

It's a steamy hot day in the summer of 1936, high in St. Vincent's Hospital in lower Manhattan. A Catholic hospital, the last one in New York, welcomes a boy born this summer who will become a Catholic someday. The hospital, long a fixture in the artists and writers section of the city called Greenwich Village, will be outlasted by this baby.

With no air conditioning in those days, his mother will tell her son how terribly uncomfortably she awaited his arrival. Seventy-five years later meteorologists in the midst of a July heat wave will say the New York summer of '36 remains the hottest on record. No wonder Bobby delights in steamy days of summer.

And it's no surprise his mother seriously hates baseball. His father plays in Prospect Park in Brooklyn when she feels her time is near. She must call herself a cab from their first home, an apartment high in downtown Knickerbocker Village, to reach the hospital in time.

Bobby arrives before two other boys in the family that starts in New York but settles in New Jersey a year after he is born. The conventional wisdom: when you have a kid you move to the "country." His father, born in Brooklyn and working on Wall Street, considers anything west of the Hudson River to be country if not the wilderness. To his mother, born and raised across the Hudson River in East Orange, New Jersey means certified gentrified civilization.

The couple buys a new two-bedroom house on Riverside Drive in the Union County town of Cranford, facing the Rahway River. Within easy commuting distance to the city, the five-room clapboard white cottage in the bedroom community seems like a good idea. They learn never again to reside on roads with a liquid name. The river floods every spring and seeps into their cellar. It even joins the joists that support the first floor. One spring a teenage boy in a canoe tips over and drowns in their driveway.

The rest of the year things go swimmingly there for the little kid, although shortly he must share the place with one, and then another brother. His mother makes a game of mealtimes. Broccoli becomes trees. Mashed potato mountains and valleys feature a lake of gravy floating in the middle. Liver? It's out of bounds in this game.

She reads to him regularly and frequently shoos him outdoors for "fresh air." Like other little kids of the era, he freely wanders his world—two doors from Normandy Avenue at the corner to the woods at the dead end of Riverside Drive. She sends him to bed before seven-thirty but with a story, then lets him listen to the Lone Ranger on the radio until eight.

She sends him to nursery school and kindergarten of course, and when he begins to read and draw pictures, she tells him he is talented and he believes her.

She went to nursing school, is a strong swimmer and merited a medal for perfect attendance over twelve years of Presbyterian Sunday School but seldom takes him to church.

His athletic father, only five-five but stocky and built like a bar-rel, still plays a lot of baseball and teaches him the game. In the big backyard it's choke up, heads up, keep your eye on the ball and what am I going to do if it comes to me. He's a Dodgers fan of course and tells the boy he can either be one or move to an orphanage. In the forties and early fifties when the Dodgers fail in the fall the boy of-ten will feel the orphanage a better choice.

Another lesson: Because the short dad survived in a tough Brook-lyn neighborhood, he figures his son will not loom over possible ad-versaries, and so advises him to use any means available if bullied, including wielding an equalizing rock or a stick of wood. The advice will come in especially handy in grade school.

Dad loves a thick, rare, charcoal-broiled steak and French fries and on Saturday nights often takes Bobby and his mother to Snuffy's Steak House in Scotch Plains. A babysitter, Marie Perusse, Bobby calls Ri Ri, minds one baby brother and then another.

To start each day, his father drinks a tumbler full of several raw eggs. On fall Saturdays, saws then splits fireplace wood from the trees down the street with a maul and wedges. He lugs a wagon full of logs up the sidewalk with Bobby on top. He rakes piles of leaves for jumping into and builds snowmen. He dropkicks watermelon-shaped footballs and plays golf and handball. At the end of the day he drinks beer from a German stein on the mantle over the fireplace and sips homemade grape wine from a keg in the cellar. He smokes cigars from his humidor and selects Kaywoodie, meerschaum and other clay or briar pipes from his rack. He hears Gabriel Heater reports the news on the Mutual Network ("There's good news to-night!") and then Stan Lomax giving the sports report on WOR. That console radio often also broadcasts Dodgers baseball and West Point football games against Navy and Notre Dame.

If his young son falls and skins a knee and sobs his dad scolds him, saying "You want something to cry for?" When Bobby hesitates to try something new he tells the boy just keep trying. To give the boy confidence he tells him "Everybody's pants go on one leg at a time."

Weekdays, his father commutes to Wall Street, driving his '36 Ford three-window coupe to the railroad station in Elizabeth or riding his bicycle equipped with a four-cycle Whizzer motor to the station in Cranford.

The big backyard provides fun for the preschooler, with a swing and sandbox, shaded by a huge oak tree that hovers over the house. His mother fears it will fall on the house in a windstorm but seventy-five years later it still stands. Next door lives a playmate, Danny Rearick, the same age, soon to be a kindergarten classmate at Cleveland School.

On the first day, the two of them pose for a picture, each sporting a striped polo shirt over shorts and polished brown leather shoes with high socks. Every day they walk the sidewalk to school together across Normandy Place, along the winding river. They stop for a while under a horse chestnut tree to pick and peg them at the Rahway ducks. After school they watch older kids at Cleveland clash with the Catholic boys of St. Michael's school, just across the street.

Danny is Bobby's best pal.

And also, a partner in a perfect crime.

Chapter Six

A Favor After All

One fine day both of them, at age five, decide there would be no finer thing than to roast cookies Danny filched from his kitchen. They agree there's no other place better than their stick lean-to hideout in the woodlot down the street by the swimming hole in the river. One strike-anywhere wooden match taken from the drawer of the end table holding Bobby's father's well-stocked pipe rack and humidor full of Webster Fancytail cigars would get the cooking going.

Sure does.

Sparks and cinders quickly ascend from sticks on the ground to roar through the roof. Despite desperate attempts to beat them out with an old broom, their fire defies control, becomes a conflagration, demolishes the den and soon is spreading to the sapling scrub forest.

The only reasonable thing to do is run five minutes for home.

When Bobby arrives, he breathlessly announces to his mother, for the first time in his life, that he needs a nap. He races up the stairs to his bedroom. He hears sirens.

"Bobby, Bobby," his mother calls, come see the fire engines going by."

"I'm too tired," the lover of fire trucks lies.

It's the perfect arson crime. Nobody suspects them. Bob never confesses. If it ever entered a conscience, it departs when developers clear the land for housing.

The two of them rationalize they did the town a favor.

Near the swimming hole, the river supplies nests of duck eggs which Bobby and dad seek for omelets in the spring; trout fishing in the summer and ice skating in the winter. The boy falls through thin ice into the freezing but shallow water several times. He wades out easily and in his wet and heavy wool snow suit staggers across the street to home.

He lands few trout because sometimes the fish slip off his so-called fishhook because it bears no barb. His mother insists he utilize a safety pin instead. He never feels a hook in a finger.

And he owns a pony. Or he thinks so. In reality, when he wears a cowboy suit and rides Smoky on Saturdays at a stable on the other side of town it is only a rental for an hour or so.

On other Saturday mornings he accompanies his father to his Wall Street office. They take the train to Hoboken, then the Hudson Tube and finally, an elevator. His father talks into two telephones in each hand in a cubicle behind a frosted glass door. In both English and Spanish, he sets up shipments of sugar to New York and agreements for goods to go back on the boats to Cuba and Puerto Rico. His son draws with indelible pencils on spread sheets sandwiched around carbon paper, then punches the keys of a clackety-clack typewriter. Afterward they take the subway to Brooklyn and Ebbets Field to see the Dodgers and down soft drinks, hot dogs and peanuts. Then they walk to his grandmother Rose's fancy Ocean Parkway apartment, where she tries to stuff him with a supper he dislikes, especially the bread with so-called sweet butter that tastes like lard.

Even though he has never tasted lard.

Once in a while on a Sunday afternoon his mother reluctantly agrees to go to a Brooklyn game too, although she hates baseball, especially the Dodgers, with good reason. His father is always playing baseball. He had played perpetually before they married, sometimes with the Dodgers themselves, afternoons in Prospect Park. And of course, there was that day on the way to the maternity ward.

So she carries a book and reads it right in a box seat behind the Dodgers' dugout. Invariably, some faithful Bums fan way up in the cheap seats bellows, "Hey lady, you wanna trade seats? You can see the book just as good from back here."

On another Saturday father and son see the Ringling Brothers and Barnum & Bailey Circus in Madison Square Garden on Eighth Avenue, where the gorilla named Gargantua the Great is a giant side show attraction. They sit up in the balcony, in the same seats when on another day they watch the Rangers play hockey. Sometimes they walk to the Bronx Zoo and the Museum of Natural History or subway to the aquarium in Brooklyn. A favorite lunch spot is the Automat, where the boy drops coins and pulls a sandwich and pie from the doors.

He will always dream of these days with his dad. Embedded mostly because of a balsa glider launched with a rubber band on a stick is a Day Line cruise thirty-five miles up the Hudson to Indian Point. A tribe of Indians operates an amusement park there. One day much later it will give way to a nuclear power plant. Another trip farther up the river reaches West Point, with a military parade grounds marching performance followed by a football game in Michie Stadium.

In Jersey he savors trips to the swimming pool at Rahway. He wears woolen bathing trunks that sag suggestively when heavily wet no matter how many times he tugs them up. His father also wears a woolen suit, including a tank top required for modesty by hairy-chested (or not) men. Afterward they down wonderful foot-long hot dogs at Walt's, across the way.

He attends the World's Fair in Flushing, Queens, in 1940, a quarter of a century before the next one there, which he will also see. For sure, television makes its debut in '40, but even more magical to a four-year old, so does a mechanical Elsie the Borden Cow. When he lifts her tail, she delivers a bottle of chocolate milk.

Closer to home, high school football games in Cranford, where he once drops his mittens below the bleachers, and baseball practice in the backyard bring the two of them close without bother from his brothers, one a toddler, the other an infant.

Sometimes on a Sunday his father's mother visits from Brooklyn, driven by his father's older brother Uncle Charlie or his Aunt Minnie's husband Uncle Al Singer, he of the sewing machine company. His Grandma Rose appears stylishly wealthy even though certainly a poor widow late in life, having scrubbed stairways as an apartment house "super" while supporting six sons and a daughter on her own.

One of those sons inadvertently makes her a lot of money one horrible day.

Chapter Seven

The Violinist

Son Rudolph, a few years older than Bobby's father, plays the violin like no other his age. Acclaimed the nation's finest young violinist of the era, he performs on command for President Calvin Coolidge and in Paul Whiteman's orchestra.

Bob's vivacious great-aunt Jenny, a frequent concert goer and patron, introduces her twenty-year-old niece, one day to become Bobby's mother, to the handsome musician. They become an item. Rudy teachers her to play.

In these Depression years few people will pay for a concert ticket as they did in 1929 when he made his solo debut at the acoustically acclaimed Steinway Hall after years as a student of the renowned virtuoso Albert Vertchamp. So, he plays in movie orchestras and performs as a concert master on a Los Angeles radio program. He drives his new car home from Hollywood to Brooklyn for a family visit in April of 1933. In June he receives a telegram from Vertchamp to come back to California for an important gig. His father advises him to take the train instead of making the long drive. Between trains in Chicago, he visits the 1933 World's Fair.

At the fair, Rudy boards a sight-seeing airplane, an amphibious Sikorsky. It leaves from Lake Michigan near the spot that one day will be the site of the vast McCormick Place convention center.

The plane crashes and burns in the nearby town of Glenview, killing all seven persons aboard.

A life insurance policy pays his mother $20,000, maybe more, a lot of money in those days. So expensive Sheraton style furniture fills her apartment, and she wears fashionable clothes, topped by a fox fur stole. Its head bares sharp teeth that bite her grandson in the neck when she visits and administers her compulsory hug.

Now she's Bobby's grandmother.

She fills that role because Rudy will become his uncle post-mortem after his mother meets his younger brother at the funeral and decides he is the next best thing. Two violins adorned with ribbons hang side by side in their home. They will always remain silent and remind her she will never play again and never board a plane. They remind her, long after her initial shock and grief, that in her mind, the traffic manager will never measure up to the violinist.

Her marriage to the next best thing will result in the next worst thing.

Chapter Eight

Jersey's Real Country

Some Sundays in spring and summer the Cranford family drives to actual country, Lafayette, New Jersey, way out in Sussex County, not far from the Delaware water gap, to visit his mother's grandparents. They live in a shingled bungalow on a dirt road a mile off busy Route 94. The small structure sports four dormers, each facing the direction of a compass point. His great-grandfather, Frank Jones, a stubby and fringed-bald retired carpenter and slate roofer, built it himself, the dormers on display to exhibit the proud Welshman's roofing prowess.

The deep backyard features a garage and an outhouse, both with similar fancy slate roofs, plus a great big vegetable garden, bushes and two black walnut trees that one day will be worth more than the bungalow. The erstwhile privy now serves as a garden tool shed because one of the bedrooms became a plumbed modern bathroom. Gramp and Gram met and married in Pennsylvania in the '80s, then hopped on a covered wagon and drove two horses east, instead of "west young man."

Gramp drove the first car in town and now, in a newer one, often nails a few of his neighbor's chickens. Why the chickens wander across his country road he does not know while crocked when he kills them. After a Gram Jones dinner of road-kill chicken and dumplings and broccoli, and pie from the berry bushes in the backyard he and Gramp depart for a bubbling stream down the dirt road. Gramp produces a roll of twine and a pocketknife and fashions a willow limb into a limber fishing pole. He pulls a real fishhook from his vest, putting to rest that baby safety pin stuff. Inside the stem of a stream-bank bush he grabs a grub and baits it.

Soon the boy catches several small speckled trout. He proudly gives them to Gram, who fries them with bacon before they leave for Cranford. Those times will turn him into a small-stream trout fisherman for the rest of his life.

They also ring the door buzzer at the entrance hall to his mother's parents' apartment building in East Orange. This grandmother, Frances, spends most of her adulthood in garden clubs, library clubs, church clubs and just about any other kind of club she can find or will have her. That lifestyle prepares her to be a lousy cook. Her mother-in-law had lived with the family and made most of the meals and for that matter mostly raised two granddaughters. But she has left for her eternal reward, leaving her daughter -in-law alone in the kitchen. Bobby's one and only live grandfather, the portly general manager of the New Jersey Swift & Company Newark office and the father of those two girls, could play the movie double of a perfect stuffed shirt, think W.C. Fields, complete with vest, watch fob and ankle-high vici kid shoes, custom made. He calls himself a butter and egg man. He claims descent from a line of New York grocers, purportedly one who owned the first store in the city. He buys a new Buick every year.

Living with his mother, a club woman wife and two daughters, he does not relate to a little boy.

These Sunday sessions include numerous pungent old lady hugs sprinkled with lavender and powder. Between them, from the nip of the fox and scent of the other, both grandmothers unknowingly keep him at arm's length from everyone for the rest of his days, except of course for a few young girls.

Cousins and aunts and uncles occasionally appear at his home on Sundays with hand-me-down thick and itchy Harris tweed woolen knickers. Luckily, they go out of style soon and he never wears them.

On balance, it's an idyllic childhood in a new home in a nice neighborhood, with two doting parents, two baby brothers, a pony, two dogs (a dachshund and a scotty), plenty of toys and rides in the rumble seat of the three-window Ford coupe manufactured the year he was born.

It all comes to a screeching halt in May of 1942.

That's when the boy Bobby becomes Bob—the man of the family.

Chapter Nine

'You're the Man'

At thirty years old and the father of three, Henry won't have to go to war. He volunteers anyway and becomes a second lieutenant with a direct commission in the transportation corps, based on his Wall Street traffic manager duties and his night school classes at St. John's in Brooklyn.

Why would he join the army?

It's simple, he says.

He wants to kill Adolf Hitler.

On a Sunday afternoon the neighbors assemble around the brick fireplace in the backyard for a sendoff. He's the only one of them going. They are all too old, too married and unmotivated. Mr. Rearick in the brick colonial next door is an air raid warden—that's about all anybody else does. Nobody knows how long Henry will be gone. He says it will be for the "duration."

Monday morning, he leaves for a far-off battle.

But on Monday night he comes home.

With the onset of war, furious training schedules overwhelm facilities at Fort Hamilton in Brooklyn, so his military career begins by commuting there to a day job. Then suddenly one morning, he will leave to ship across the Atlantic to England and train for what will be the invasion of Normandy.

That will become D-Day.

He stands his not-quite six-year-old son aside next to his bed. He squats eye to eye and seems very serious, almost on the verge of tears.

"While I'm gone, I'll depend on you to take care of your mother and brothers," he tells him.

"Now you are the man of the family."

It's a lot to drop on the shoulders of a six-year-old but he readily accepts the role. He plays it confidently and responsibly and relishes his authority. His brothers will come to resent him, and more than once remind him he is not their father. Their big brother will issue orders and become onerous in their eyes. He just wants to keep them out of trouble that he would have to account for but sometimes is overzealous. Mindful of his father's charge, he develops traits of preparedness and caution.

To his two brothers, there is no doubt about it.

He's a killjoy.

The war will rage for a third of Bob's life, until he reaches nine and fourth grade. A lot happens to father and son on both sides of the ocean. Hardly any of it any good. As it will for so many other Americans, the war will disrupt the direction of their lives forever.

The first direction, for the family with no father goes north.

When she worked in the Newark public library before her wedding, Dorothy befriended coworker Zelda Norcross, who later bought an inn way up in the ski resort town of Stowe, Vermont, not far from the Canadian border. The two of them keep in touch.

"Why don't you move up here and spend the war?" Zelda writes her. It seems like a pretty good idea.

With German submarines already patrolling the Jersey shore, sometimes near underwater defensive nets, many in the metropolitan area fear potential invasion. If the Japanese can hit Hawaii, couldn't the Nazis attack across the Atlantic?

Vermont is the sticks, the outback, the hinterland. If New Jersey contends as the country, Vermont clinches the title of authentic wilderness.

Chapter Ten

No Nazis Here

So Dorothy sells the house on Riverside Drive. Sight unseen, simply from an ad in the *New York Times,* she rents a brown-shingled bungalow four miles from Rutland up the East Pittsford Road which leads, to nobody's surprise, to East Pittsford, Vermont, a backwater burgh if you ever saw one. She has never even visited the state. And she doesn't write her husband to tell him until the deed is done in more ways than one.

But, she supposes, Nazis will never storm the Green Mountains. Certainly not East Pittsford.

On a broiling July day mother and sons board the train at Grand Central for a three-hundred-mile trip to Rutland, five short of their ultimate destination. Bob's mother wears a dark blue hat with a matching veil to hide cheeks swollen with the mumps, a gift from her new man of the family, who contracted the ailment a couple of weeks ago.

The town law requires quarantine, but the movers load their furniture, the closing goes off on schedule and the train whistle beckons. So off they go—mother, toddler brother, two-month-old baby and, of course, the man of the family.

Their new landlord, tall and lanky widower Bill Chapin, meets them at the station in Rutland. He loads their several suitcases in a '41 Ford "Woodie" station wagon and they set off for the bungalow four miles up the East Pittsford Road. You might think this is one of those corny old movies, but Bill Chapin is no hick. A Dartmouth grad and successful dairy farmer, he has sold his cows. The bungalow was the home of his hired man. Bill Junior literally flew off to war. A B-24 pilot, he was shot down by Luftwaffe over Yugoslavia, parachuted safely but was captured and is now imprisoned in a Nazi camp that will become the model for the play and movie Stalag Seventeen and the television program Hogan's Heroes. He will lose a leg, and after the war become a fashion model, author and professor who one day will work at as a reporter both at the *Rutland Herald* and *Stars & Stripes* in Tokyo about twenty years before the man of the family will sit at the same desks.

The next day Mr. Chapin, so far lacking grandchildren, presents Bob with a recurved longbow, a quiver of arrows and a leather arm protector. They hike to the meadow for an archery lesson. Over the summer Bob aims many arrows at a bulls-eye target pinned to a pair of big hay bales.

In the woods behind the house the now seven-year-old and his nearly four-year-old brother wear soldier suits. Armed with toy rifles and a wooden machine gun on a tripod they aim at birds and squirrels and Nazis. In the bungalow they listen intently as their mother reads censored photostat letters that arrive from overseas, probably from England. They help their mother dip oranges in paraffin, hoping to preserve them after she mails them across the Atlantic.

Daily the nervous mother and sons warily devour the war news on the radio. They don't know Bob's dad commands a duck boat on D-Day, delivers troops and then himself to Omaha Beach and will be wounded in the knee, shoulder and head, and spend time in the hospital in England before recovering to command a Red Ball Express convoy under fire through France and Germany.

The boys want Kellogg's Pep breakfast cereal instead of Wheaties, which they prefer, so they can open the box and collect and assemble cardboard models of U.S. war planes, especially the favorite P-38 Lightning. With less commitment, ex-suburban, now country boy Bob rides a horse on wooded trails with ten-year-old Barbara Walker, whose parents own a nearby farm. Smoky in Cranford supplied experience and confidence.

September, as it always will, kills summer fun and means his second school and second grade at Barstow in Chittenden, about five miles away. Reached with a ride with one of the teachers, a nearby neighbor, Miss Cram, it includes grades one through twelve. It means learning to play with backwoods country kids. They never knew kindergarten, unheard of in much of Vermont, let alone the nursery school which Bob attended in Jersey. Descriptions of New York City events and attractions, and delights in Jersey such as "The Duggan Man" with his cheesecake or the Good Humor Man with his ice cream truck makes him a snob and showoff. And one of Vermont's early flatlanders. His desire to assimilate will be as difficult as it is for a fleeing undocumented alien from a foreign land. .

One cold morning in the cloak room he unbuckles rubber boots, mentioning their now in Vermont effete Jersey name.

Galoshes.

That word brings peals of derisive laughter.

"Galoshes? What are you talking about? Those are overshoes you jerk."

Pronunciation causes more problems. He says he has a "dawg," an English Setter (who joined the scotty but not the dachshund named Hansy (since deceased because of a car on Riverside Drive). Classmates teach him he really has a "dahg" that drinks "wahter." He thinks one pronunciation is as good as another but is incorrect of course. Over time his accent will settle somewhere in the middle, and nobody will guess where he comes from no matter where he lives. There be so many more moves that he will come from many places. But not yet.

At Barstow, an elaborate brick and marble building named for the philanthropist who funded it, the high school home economics girls prepare hot lunches in an equally perfect kitchen. But the meals, neither hot nor well prepared, assail the palate. Bob avoids their cupcakes, alternately soggy and heavy or dry and hard.

The neighbor teacher, Miss Cram, careens her car around dirt road curves when she drives him to school with one eye on the road.

The other is glass.

She becomes his private tutor but lessons at the living room upright piano don't last long. He learns to play only one piece, *Good King Wenceslas*, because it needs only two notes. He'd rather play ball.

Oh yeah, his mother doesn't drive at all. She owns no car. Back in Jersey, on the way home from passing her driver test, she drove through a stop sign and t-boned another Ford because, she said, she was afraid if she stopped, she wouldn't be able to get it to go again. Happily, only a few dings damaged each car.

A policeman drove her home. She vowed never to drive again. So, her husband sold the Ford before he went overseas.

Trips to Rutland to buy groceries now depend on "taxi" payment to the milkman Donald Russell, who also delivers them when she phones an order to the Rutland Boston Market store. When his brother Steven, the four-year-old, develops pneumonia the milkman drives him to the Rutland hospital and brings him home two weeks later.

Chapter Eleven

Pearl Street and the Principal

With summer, Barstow schoolwork succumbs, freeing the boy for fun. The family moves a few miles west, to Pittsford, still in the sticks, but on Route Seven, the major north-south Vermont highway. It's a rented downstairs apartment in another brown-shingled building, once a farmhand's home, behind the big Burroughs former farmhouse, backed by cow pastures and hay fields, and now a guest home, a tourist place. The Walker farm across the road, inhabited by Barbara and her parents, holds more convenient horseback riding. Directly behind the farm lies the man-made Pittsford Pond, dammed as a reservoir for Rutland to its south. A boat with oars tied to a tree seems available to anybody who wants to row it. Bob spends hours in pursuit of perch in the pond, but he and brother Steve also find time to snag and release frogs in bogs on their side of the road.

By the time school starts in September, they reach a Vermont semblance of civilization when they move again, to Rutland, population about 18,000. This "city" becomes the eight-year-old's fourth home, discounting the apartment in New York, when he didn't know where he was.

It's a two-story, typical, two-family apartment place built early in the century, with narrow rooms up and down to fit a narrow quarter-acre lot. Bob's family occupies the first floor.

One winter night the house on Pearl Street makes the whole family unaware of where they are.

Bob and Steve play Chinese checkers on the rug in the living room when they start to develop headaches. Steve, kneeling, pitches forward and collapses on the carpet, unconscious. Bob yells to his mother in the kitchen. She rouses Steven and rushes Bob and baby brother Billy out into the night air. The furnace leaks coal gas and carbon monoxide. Mrs. Stapleton across the street calls an ambulance. It's the first time in a hospital for Bob since St. Vincent's. It will be another sixty years before he stays in another.

After a night on a hill in the wooden Nichols Street hospital the boys and their mother go home.

The southern end of Pearl Street terminates at Crescent Street, and on that corner resides a red-faced, raw-boned nuisance of a neighbor for Bob, his brother Steve and their schoolmates. George Hurley personifies the perfect bully. He will become an even bigger pain for the community, the county, the state and even the United States Army.

Right now, though, George, only eleven or twelve, tosses Steve's scooter into the deepest hole in Tenney Brook. The following winter he throws a snowball embedded with a stone and hits the poor kid in the head. Bleeding, Steve comes home crying. His mother swabs the cut with cotton and iodine, which makes him wail even more.

The furious mother marches right up to the miscreant's house. She confronts Mrs. Hurley on the front porch.

"Not my Georgie. Georgie would never do such a thing," the bully's mother protests. "My Georgie is a good boy."

Her Georgie not only did it, he advances to such things much worse, things his mother cannot deny, things that will leave Georgie out of her obituary list of survivors.

Things that will get him disowned by his entire family.

This thing, however, is enough to make Bob vow that one day he will make George Hurley pay. He will get even.

Third grade means Lincoln School, Bob's third one since Cleveland in Cranford. And then before it's time to fire up that defective coal furnace on Pearl Street, the boys and their mother move again to a two-family house on Church Street, similar in architecture to Pearl but newer and better appointed, next door to a corner grocery. Just a couple of blocks away, it requires no further school switch.

George Hurley lives no farther away really, with Tenney Brook just as close, as it wends its way southwest. Church Street offers new adventures, being closer to Rotary Field, with its baseball diamonds and tennis courts and arts and crafts sessions in the summer—and ice skating on the flooded field in the winter. Bob learns to swim in the adjacent municipal pool. The downside: he must take his brothers there too and keep a close eye on the younger guy, Billy, in the kiddie pool. Then there's Steven, who dives into the nine-foot end even though he knows not how to swim. Bob pulls him to the gutter and up.

The war drags on through third grade and Bob, a Cub Scout, collects newspapers, balls of string, tinfoil from gum wrappers, grease saved in a Crisco can at the back of the stove for explosives and even milkweed pods for life jackets to support the troops.

And then one afternoon late in May of '45, just weeks after the Hitler's suicide and the Nazis surrender, teacher Miss O'Neil tells the nearly nine-year-old to report to Miss Burns, the principal, who also teaches sixth grade. The boy imagines only the worst. It's not just being summoned by the principal for alleged infraction of the rules or discipline. It could be about his father in the war.

Usually stern, she shows some compassion as she commands the boy to stand by her at her desk in front of the big kids of the class. Then, she puts an arm around his shoulders. All the sixth graders already know what she is going to say next.

"Your daddy is home!" she announces loudly.

He bursts into tears, elated but embarrassed. He jumps off the chair, races out the classroom door, down the hall, out the double brass doors and runs a block away to Church Street and home. It has been three years, a third of his life, since his dad left home in New Jersey to kill Hitler, who has finally killed himself.

And now his father is home!

Chapter Twelve

Post-War Euphoria

For Bob's dad, it's never so true that "you can't go home again," because his wife sold his. For any G.I. there is nothing better after a war than finally to go home again. No longer having the home he left in Cranford, after his discharge from Fort Devens in Massachusetts, his dad hitchhikes in his army officer uniform to Rutland, the first time he's ever been here. Because of his wounds and purple heart, his overseas combat, and because he is the married father of three, he is one of the first to be separated from the service.

After a long European war the reunion with his family is fabulous, home or no home.

School lets out for a magical summer, just like the old days in New Jersey. Father and son fish for trout in Tenney Brook. His dad pulls out a fat eighteen-incher, which they watch swim in the bathtub until his mother bakes and serves it for supper. They play baseball around the corner at the high school field. His father, still only 34, wows the practicing varsity team when he hits one 450 feet to the roof of the school, something they have never seen. Father and son swim at the city pool as the lifeguard gasps. The barrel-chested dad's lungs let him swim the length of it submerged.

In a word, the summer goes swimmingly, highlighted by the front yard dancing and banging of pots and pans in August after two atomic bombs obliterate two Japanese cities and Hirohito surrenders on the U.S.S. Missouri to General MacArthur. The western world rejoices, no more so than Bob, because his father is finally here.

But is he really in Rutland to stay?

Could this be home?

Soon Bob will wonder where home ever will be.

His city slicker father learned to like suburban New Jersey, because at least he could commute to New York. But the wilds of Vermont? The backwoods? The sticks and hicks, the hinterland? The jerkwater town? There is no job here for him. The boy's mother has learned to love Vermont and wants to stay here, but his father feels he just can't. Where will he work? What will he do? The parents argue about the present and the future.

His son's euphoria is about to evaporate.

His own future?

An army brat.

In September his father thumbs his way back to Fort Devens, re-ups and is sent to Fort Mason in San Francisco. He'll be a career man. The family soon follows. That means fourth grade, started at Lincon School with the stern Mrs. Shippe, will continue a week later on the west coast in still another school. It's a pattern now—another year, another new cast of classmates. Fourth grade and fourth school. And another "home." San Francisco will be his sixth address, not counting Manhattan.

It also means a five-day train trip for the family of four, but one that overall is fun. The Rutland Railroad milk run to Grand Central traverses the same track that took them to Vermont three years earlier. Then it's a cab ride to Penn Station and the gleaming 20th Century Limited, with its Pullman cars and upper and lower berths. A steward in a crisp white coat serves a fancy dinner in the dining car, complete with gleaming silver and china on a white linen tablecloth.

But back in their seats after supper there is soon to be drama, provided by the three-year old. When the porter appears to transform the bench seats into beds, his baby brother Billy, now three, excitedly announce to everyone in the car the arrival of only the second black person he has ever seen. He reveals his limited his literary background.

"Mommy! Mommy! he exclaims. Here comes Little Black Sambo!"

More to come. He stars in yet another scene. Begging to sit on the upper berth, his mother boosts him there, only to have him throw up on her head and hair.

The click-clack of the wheels on the track send them to sleep quickly after a long day. The next thing they know they are nearing Chicago, once again in the dining car, enjoying an elegant breakfast.

So here they are in the nation's number two city, in huge Union Station, almost as busy as Grand Central and Penn. His mother sighs. Just thirteen years earlier Rudy checked his violin and other luggage here and went to the World's Fair

And died.

She and Rudy's nephews must wait all day for the train that will take them the rest of the way. They lounge on long benches in the morning, the mother with magazines and the kids with comics and puzzle books, but boredom takes its toll. So after sandwiches in the station the mother takes them to a movie. Bob enjoys "The Big Sleep," with Bogart and Bacall even though he doesn't really "get" it. It means a nice big nap for the younger brothers (and a merciful respite for their exhausted mother).

You can go Southern Pacific (the scenic route) or Union Pacific (the northern route). They wind up on the Southern, which takes them by Great Salt Lake, the Grand Canyon, past the Painted Desert and the Petrified Forest, down to Albuquerque where Navajos toil on the tracks, and, finally, up to San Francisco.

Several stops along the way give Bob a chance to walk their English setter, who rides in a crate in the baggage car. The three boys often visit him there and let him out to run around in the car.In Cheyenne, Bob buys a red felt pennant with a picture of a cowboy and the legend "Frontier Days." Actually, two are stuck together and when the train pulls away it concerns him that he has cheated the station store clerk. One day he will return one of them. And he never guesses that on another day much later he will be a reporter covering Frontier Days for the *Wyoming Eagle* morning daily.

The Pullmans, more popular than the fledgling airlines, often feature celebrity fellow passengers, including Two-Ton Baker, a Chicago radio personality, who sings one of his specialties, "I'm a Lonely Little Petunia in an Onion Patch."

Also in the car, Leo Carrillo, who played the Cisco Kid in the movies, befriends the young family, buys them brunch on arrival in San Francisco, then gives them tickets to a matinee. He stars on the stage as the Kid's sidekick, Pancho.

After the show Bob's mother takes the three boys high up in the children's department of the Emporium, a big department store on Market Street, and buys them all cowboy boots.

If you are going to be out west, she says, you must look like you belong.

Chapter Thirteen
San Francisco and Back

The blue Belton setter, formally named "Henry's Tavistock Fitzgerald," joined the family in East Pittsford while Bob's father, who likes Fitzgerald ale, trained for D-Day in Tavistock England. The dog, of grand champion parentage, really just called Fitzy, gets confined to a kennel under the Golden Gate Bridge because the military rules the housing on Contra Costa Boulevard off limits to canines. Fitzy and the family both whine and whimper between visits that feel like going to see some felon. For all they can tell Fitzy might as well be on offshore Alcatraz.

Upon their arrival at their new home, it's also temporarily off limits to their furniture, still en route from the east coast. The moving van travels slower than the train. Army cots and paper plates on a wooden dining table packing crate will do for a week before the truck arrives. The boys like camping in their new home. The parents do not.

Connected carports flank the duplex facing Contra Costa Boulevard. A common rear yard contains a coin laundry for all the residents, playground equipment for all the kids and lots of rules and regulations, certainly no tunnels in the sandy soil for roads and toy trucks.

This officer housing is considered choice, but not by Bob. He can't avoid it years later, because he winds up in similar quarters in the future and even in barracks as an airman much later. Suffice to say that as soon as possible he never again lives like that.

Otherwise however, San Francisco supplies fun. Bob learns to shoot pool in the officers' club and watches Nazi prisoner POWs stabbing discarded papers on the Green at Fort Mason. He also spends time in the fort gymnasium, where his special services officer father coaches sports teams and otherwise oversees athletic activity, based on his pre-war baseball playing. Bob sees all the main sights, from A to Z, including Alcatraz and the zoo, the cable cars, Fisherman's Wharf, the Golden Gate over the kennel and the tunnel under the Twin Peaks. It's also where Bob first gets published—with drawings in the *Oakland Tribune* across the bay.

Fourth grade in a fourth new school doesn't last long. Bob never makes a friend. Most of his classmates hail from Oklahoma because their families fled the infamous Dust Bowl, or from Mexico, for work here for their parents.

In April his father ships out to Korea, for reconstruction duty. Not even officers' families can go to war-torn and primitive Korea, formerly enslaved by the Japanese, who raped its natural resources. Reconstruction includes planting trees, because the Japanese denuded the hills by lumbering. That resulted in erosion so detrimental that cutting one down has become a capital offense.

So after only several months in San Francisco the mother and sons and setter retrace their footsteps, pawprints and railroad tracks back to Rutland. There is the usual stop in Cheyenne where Bob amazes the woman in the shop at the station. He returns the second pennant and tells her it had been stuck to the one he had bought.

Even more amazing: they move to a house on Grove Street in the Lincoln School district. For only the second time in his life Bob will attend, for the rest of the year, a school with classmates he already knows. What a delight!

The two-family house resembles the one they left a block away on Church Street. The new address has its moments, including the day Bob dislocates his shoulder during a pillow fight with Steve. Luckily, the upstairs tenant, Dr. William Brislin, quickly yanks his arm and clicks the shoulder into its socket

Steve shows promise in sales when the rabbi's wife next door buys a box of his Christmas cards. Bob tries to sell enough Victory Garden vegetable seeds to win a pair of New Zealand White rabbits but falls short. He does succeed in stringing a tin can telephone to next door pal Eddy Bartlett's bedroom from his own.

Edward (Baldy) Brand, a secondhand furniture store owner, delivers a chair when nobody is home and lingers to refresh himself. He leaves a note in the refrigerator: "Brand was here and drank your beer."

There will be much more to hear from him.

Up Grove Street, the country club boasts a tantalizing swinging rope "monkey bridge" over East Creek. Only golfers are allowed to cross although all the neighborhood boys try it too. Farther up the street, at Patch's Dam, Bob catches bullhead in the spring before trout season opens and perch in summer.

On the way there, old man Vaughan sits on his stone wall at the street in front of his mansion. Herman Vaughan made his fortune years earlier at his Ticonderoga, New York, paper mill. He developed a paper bag that opened square on the bottom, winning the minds and hearts and cash of the many sugar refining companies in New York City. They thus abandoned the costlier muslin sacks they had bought for years. Retired now, he likes to listen with his gigantic brass ear horn to the kids who come by.

Behind him Bob gets a glimpse of a girl with golden hair sitting next to a glass greenhouse filled with flowers. Her father is the old man's chauffeur. She lives upstairs in the carriage house garage behind the mansion. He sees her reading on a white marble bench by a goldfish pond.

Ten years from now he will sit on the same bench beside the "Breck Girl."

Without even moving September and fifth grade mean school number five. He blames it on a great-grandmother who raised his mother in the continuous absence of her clubby mother. Nuns in a convent school raised Bob's great granny although not a Catholic. That upbringing inspires Bob's mother to enroll her older boys in the closest Catholic school, St. Peter's. In the absence of their father, she feels her boys will benefit from the brand of discipline she knows only nuns can dispense.

Of course, Bob is not Catholic. His mother, a faithful Presbyterian in her youth, married a man who claimed to be an atheist, although teary whenever inside a church. The inside of the only Presbyterian church Bob knew was stark, simple, plain, whitewashed and wearisome. Hymns raised to heaven by the congregation seemed no match for music on the radio.

He joins his fellow fifth graders in the Romanesque St. Peter's Church. Many votive candles, the shadows they cast over large statues and an overall aura of history and mystery convince him he is in the presence of God. His teacher, Sister Mary Perpetua, says he may read or draw pictures during religion class, but he eavesdrops. The more he hears the more he wants to know. In February of 1946, Father Michael Demasi, the curate of St. Peter's, baptizes Bob and his brothers to create three new Catholics. Several years later their mother will also undergo the waters.

Now Bob's got religion, but he can't complete fifth grade at St. Peter's.

Months before the end of the school year, his father returns to California, his Korea assignment complete. Once again the mother and sons cross the country by Pullman to San Francisco, with their ultimate destination to be Rodeo on San Pablo Bay, across the water from wine country. The army officer, now a major, commutes to Camp Stoneman in Pittsburg, twenty miles east.

The small town of Rodeo some twenty miles north of San Francisco and its available housing, single-story stucco triplexes stuck together under typical California tile roofs in the suffocating heat of spring and summer, offer no particular fun. Not the least of it is Bob's sixth school, where he will complete the fifth grade.

To beat the blistering heat Bob crosses the dangerous four-lane main drag and the railroad tracks to dip into the bay. He comes home wearing black and blue oil leaked from tankers and the tanks they filled, denying he dove into the forbidden murky depths. He gets hotter playing ball with the Cub Scouts, hardball rules using a softball and softball infield against other Cub packs up and down the bay, mostly in Richmond. Little League remains in the future

Pro baseball in Oakland means the Oaks of the Pacific Coast League and a pre-game meeting with Lefty O'Doul and Casey Stengel, managers of the San Francisco Seals and the Oaks, or Acorns, respectively. His father takes him down on the field to shake hands with both of them, friends from his ball-playing days in Brooklyn. Bob sees Vince DiMaggio, older than his more famous brothers, blast a ball over the fence, over the crowd behind it and out of the stadium and into the street behind center field. Longest homer he's ever seen. Probably farther than one his father ripped to the high school roof.

The overcrowded post-war public school makes him suffer through "solid sessions." In one such, a kid goes a few weeks from eight to one and the rest of the year from noon to five. No lunch breaks either way. Catholic kids win time off one afternoon a week to attend Catechism class with some nuns at their convent. Rodeo has no parochial school.

Bob makes an eventful First Communion. With no air conditioning on a steamy Sunday in May, the pastor opens the church doors wide to admit some air, but that's not all that enters. At a couple of months shy of eleven years old, convert Bob lines up conspicuously with the seven-year-old second graders. Suddenly he begins to sweat profusely, much more than the situation or temperature would produce. Fitzy has followed him to the church, and now prances down the center aisle to join him at the altar rail. Blushing blood red, Bob grabs his collar, guides him up the aisle and shoos him out the door, shutting it with a bang. Although the occasion is supposed to be solemn, the situation makes the congregation smile.

If not in school or in the bay a boy could explore the foothills and throw rocks at ground squirrels or windows of abandoned houses that turn out to be occupied, according to the cops who find Bob and two pals and make his father pay for new glass.

Meanwhile, the major and his wife squabble and battle and by June the boys and their mother once again board the train back to Vermont. Bob doesn't know all the details but he knows his mother wants to be in Vermont while his father has to be in California.

Chapter Fourteen

The Hillbilly

Returning to Rutland on short notice, the mother and sons have no home at all, so they bunk in two rooms at the downtown Hotel Berwick. It seems like fun at first, but after a couple of weeks the novelty wears thin. It's July 1947.

There remains more to Baldy Brand than that pilfered bottle of beer when he delivered a chair for their home on Grove Street. For one thing, he served as Godfather to the boys at their Baptism by Father Demasi at St. Peter's, along with Dorothy Stapleton as Godmother, she who called for help during the Pearl Street coal gas episode. Now Brand proposes to rent or sell a summer place seven miles up on Mendon Mountain. Bob's mother, remembering living in nearby East Pittsford, likes the remote location but won't take it under either arrangement without renovations and remodeling for year-round occupancy. The family moves in while Brand, a former carpenter, hires a crew and they begin to work. His mother feeds them. Brand buys them beer. Bob becomes a helper, picking up carpentry skills he will employ years later.

A new wing features a dining-family room, an expanded concrete foundation and cellar, a second bathroom with shower downstairs and a second bedroom upstairs. The remodeled kitchen looks out to a deck in the back and to a babbling little brook. A new garage, a Heatilator unit in the front room fireplace, a screened front porch and eight acres of woods and meadows fronting a few thousand acres of the Rutland City and Green Mountain National Forest complete the country homestead, which also gets a new wood and coal furnace and well pump in the basement.

After years of apartments and military housing with regimentation and rules, and rooming a month in the Berwick, it offers the boy and his brothers a great new and free environment. In some ways it reminds Bob of the home in Cranford before the war, although, for the first time since East Pittsford, four years before, they live back in the sticks.

To reach Christ the King School in Rutland, seven miles away, you must be flexible. Vermont Transit and White River Coach Line buses each cruise by the house on Route 4 once a day, usually at inopportune times. Mostly you hitchhike to and from the sixth grade (and the seventh school, unless you count Lincoln twice and consider kindergarten, which brings the total to nine.).

The townies, mostly lace-curtain Irish Catholics, haven't been more than twenty miles out of town, perhaps to swim in Lake Dunmore. Thinking themselves thoroughly sophisticated, they call Mendon Mountain Bob a hillbilly, he born in Manhattan and the veteran of four trips across the continent.

By now, after the suburb in New Jersey, the trips to New York, living in the city of San Francisco, the wilds of East Pittsford and the acreage of woods and meadows on Mendon Mountain, Bob feels at ease in any environment. He knows uniformed doormen and lumberjacks, famous bays and rivers, two oceans and tiny trout streams, fields and forests, skyscrapers and shacks, mass transportation and that which only his thumb can attract. A new school? With his experience, it's a cinch.

Except for one thing.

A new kid in school in these days seems a novelty. IBM won't transfer anybody to Vermont or much of anywhere else so it doesn't yet stand for "I've Been Moved." Right away the sixth-grade boys gang up to beat him up. After so many times in this role at so many new schools, he knows the drill. A new kid can cry and bleed with honor but not squeal. At Christ the King, however, squealing takes an odd turn.

Two boys push him down on the playground. A third tries to pull off his pants. Based on long experience, Bob anticipates some sort of confrontation. He has jammed an eight-penny nail in his belt buckle. The pants stay put. So while two punch him as he aches on the asphalt, he kicks one in the head with the hard heel of his leather shoe. That breaks his glasses and cuts his nose. His blood stops the battle.

"You dirty fighter," his attacker shouts, "I'm gonna tell on you."

Upon reflection, the dope realizes that's ridiculous. Because he dreads what his father will say about the broken glasses he decides instead to concoct a cover story.

Once they beat you up and you don't squeal you are golden—you become one of the guys, even if you root for the Dodgers instead of the Boston Braves or Red Sox. Even if you get excited about Jackie Robinson's debut with the Dodgers—not because he's black but because he helps them win the pennant.

You might ask how a student fares academically when changing schools so often. Luckily, each seems to lag the previous one. For example, he already knew the long division later introduced in fourth grade. In the sixth, he has already diagrammed sentences. When it comes to U.S. geography of course, he has already been there in person. So his grades put him at the top of his class. Some girls even called him "the brain."

The sixth-grade teacher, statuesque and stern Sister Julia Marie, wears glasses that reflect movement behind her while she faces the blackboard. She really knows who passes notes or whispers, all the way to the back of the room. She whirls around on one foot and arches one brow seemingly inches above the withering evil eye she trains upon the culprit. Quiet attentiveness ensues.

She earns Bob's eternal gratitude when she calmly announces to the class his new last name, changed due to the divorce of his parents. She delivers the news matter-of-factly, with no comment nor questions from the class. When he thanks her many years later she cannot remember the incident.

Seventh grade, Bob's second full year in the same school for the first time, features young and pretty Sister Ellen Therese, the most beloved of all the nuns in the school. She plays basketball on the playground. Turning her bib-like, starched gamp around, and with one hand hiking up the long skirt of her habit, she dribbles past a defender for a layup. In the spring, she shows the boys how to throw a curveball.

She puts up with no nonsense, however. She hears Bob whispering to a nearby pal and sentences him to sit in a seat at the back of the room. The top slat of the chair includes a couple of screws that protrude and stick him in the back. He mutters something about the screws. The nun pounces and boxes his ears, exclaiming, "You and your double-meaning words!"

She tells the class that Heaven awaits only those who are baptized. So Bob asks her if that's fair, what about good people who have never heard of the afterlife. She swallows, pauses and tells the class to open their books to chapter thirteen, and says they should "pray for the grace of a happy death." What can that possibly be, Bob wonders. It will take him another seventy years to find out that the grace she speaks of wears the clothing and customs of all the styles and morals he no longer likes and is willing to doff in favor of the hereafter.

Bob asks a lot of questions all the time. Perhaps it has something to do with the wonder of becoming acquainted with religion as a convert. In any event, he will ask many questions all his life, including lots of them as a newspaper reporter.

Fifty-seven years later he will invite Sister Ellen Therese Barry to be an honored guest at his golden high school reunion. Now well up into her eighties, she does recall Bob as irritating, but not the specifics of boxing his ears.

Chapter Fifteen

Finally, Revenge

The hated George Hurley muffs the eighth grade not once but twice at Meldon, the public junior high. His parents stick him in Christ the King where the stern and strict Sister Jane Frances roams around her room with a ruler, certain to strike. She always aims one wary eye at George, here for his third attempt.

During lunchtime soon in September, rotund seventh-grader Raymond Duffy shoots basketballs on the playground with Bob. George pounces on the kid and grabs for the ball but Duffy bends over and presses it to his belly. When George pummels Duffy on the back, Bob sees an opportunity that he has fantasized about for years. He picks up a chunk of concrete broken from the backboard post and conks the big kid on the head. George falls to the asphalt and screams as Bob stands over him, holding the concrete ready for another hit.

A couple of sisters hoisting their habit skirts come running at full speed. One wraps George's shirt around his bloody head like a bandana. The other races across the street to the rectory and calls for the curate, Father Engel. He drives George, fully conscious and crying, to the hospital emergency room where stitches close a large cut. Then he takes him home to Crescent Street and explains the situation to his mother.

Later in the afternoon Bob finds himself summoned to the office of the stern principal, Sister Imelda, accompanied by the curate. They pretend to seem very serious and she tells him he has done something terrible, regardless of the circumstances. He should be ashamed she says.

He's actually elated.

Sister Imelda always admonished miscreants with her favorite aphorism, "A word to the wise should be sufficient." Not this time. She says she will deal with him later. He's not worried. Usually if he got in trouble with a nun he was in more trouble with his mother. Not this time. She has never forgotten George Hurley.

The next day, Mrs. Hurley decides to pull her "Georgie" out of Christ the King, saying he is not safe there. The principal and the priest breathe a sigh of relief, along with Sister Jane Frances, sure one of their shared prayers is answered. Bob ponders for days what his punishment will be but somehow it must have slipped their minds. Christ the King becomes George's last conventional school, public or private. But his further misdeeds, of which there will be many, gain him admission fifty miles north to the state reform school in Vergennes.

Sister Jane Frances knows "only" forty-seven students occupy the seventh-grade classroom but in the graduating class of 1950 she wants fifty occupied desks. She will pursue two more pupils from Meldon and one from out of town. Also, her desire for a resounding chancel choir drives her to Shanghai every supposed songbird not chosen to serve on the altar. Her great hymn choices, all in Latin, include lots of Gregorian Chant.

With the rest of the choir, Bob will memorize and sing every word (off key), a major reason he will come to despise the changes of the Second Vatican Council, which eliminate the Latin Mass. Fifteen years later Bob will cringe at the "vernacular" singing of Kumbaya during Mass in New Jersey. Afterword, he asks the pastor in perfect English whose vernacular that is and explains that Sister Jane Frances, blessed by death long ago, would have been devastated.

The eighth-grade nun provides no fun for anyone, but Bob earns straight *A* grades and the highest scores on religion tests. At graduation the convert who devilishly confused several nuns along the way will win the coveted scholastic religion prize with pin, conspicuously noted in the printed program.

He plays baseball and basketball (the latter not very well) on the eighth-grade Catholic Youth Organization teams, wearing new uniforms and satin warm-ups provided by Father Engel, who serves as coach. Key games pit Christ the King against cross-town rival St. Peter's and its shanty Irish and Italian kids. When CKS wins, the priest piles his team into his Ford coupe, buys them ice cream at Seward's Dairy Bar and drops them off at home. When they lose at St. Peter's Field or the Knights of Columbus gym, he lets them walk.

Hitching rides to and from school challenges the boy, as does much work at home on the mountain. The brothers lug logs from fallen and standing dead trees in the forest across the brook over a bridge Bob built as a Boy Scout project. Bob and Steve seize each end of a two-man saw, producing great piles of fuel to feed a gluttonous fireplace and furnace. Bill is strong enough to stack the stuff. Their mother insists on a crackling fire under the mantle every evening, even in July, because mountain temperatures are cool.

Every August the water level in the well falls too low to reach the pipe to the electric pump in the basement. Bob lowers a rope to lifts bucket after bucket, which he hauls fifty yards to the downstairs bathroom and wringer washing machine.

What is not challenging, but really easy? Living in the same house for years. Going to the same grade school and graduating from a high school with the same kids for seven straight years. School stability works well. Before living in Mendon, he refrained from making friends because he feared he soon would move. Now he makes long-term pals and looks forward to attending high school with them at Mount St. Joseph Academy.

But the CKS principal, Sister Imelda, secretly fond of Bob since he conked George Hurley, nearly messes things up with the best of intentions.

She gets him a full scholarship to exclusive St. John's Prep. He dutifully rides a bus to Boston and spends a weekend in Danvers as a guest of the school as if they were trying to recruit him.

On Monday, he tells her thanks but no thanks.

The prospect of changing schools once again, without necessity, no matter how prestigious St. John's may be, is abhorrent. Besides, his now-single mother needs him at home—not just to help with his brothers while she works as a chef, but also to hold part-time jobs and contribute to the household expenses.

Now, as never before, as his father could never foresee, he is the man of the family.

Contribute he does. In the summer he paints the bottom and sides of a concrete swimming pool over the mountain in Pittsfield. He cuts firewood and brush for Mendon neighbors and digs fence post holes for an ex-gangster at his horse farm. He helps build houses in a Rutland development—by shoveling sand into a cement mixer for fifty cents an hour. In early autumn, he hitchhikes only halfway home to pick apples at ten cents a bushel, then thumbs a ride the rest of the way. He helps deliver furniture for his Godfather Baldy Brand, including helping to cart cast iron stoves up three flights of stairs.

At Christmastime he opens the door for customers at Wilson's music store and plays 45 rpm records of carols and other holiday tunes that blare onto the street so many times that he dislikes hearing them for the rest of his life. For twenty-five cents an hour.

He follows that with fifty-cents-an-hour stock boy service at an independent grocery, the Boston Market, for a year until he's sixteen. That age qualifies him for a similar position at a chain store paying seventy-five cents an hour. Then his knack for art earns a fee for creating barbecue aprons for a horse camp—which leads to starting his own business. That will become an obsession lasting for seventy more years and make him an acclaimed worldwide expert sought on several continents.

All because he acquires a pair of New Zealand Red rabbits.

Chapter Sixteen

The Scout

Work is not work if you love it. That's the case when he writes for the *Rutland Herald*. When he covers the MSJ basketball team he earns seventy-five cents an hour, the minimum wage. That includes travel time to and from out-of-town games and long pauses while he hunts and pecks on the Royal standard typewriter, trying to make the eleven o'clock first edition deadline. Even though he gives most of what he makes to his mother, owed alimony and child support that never arrives, he always has money in his pocket.

His father, now remarried in California to a woman with six kids, can be arrested if he sets foot in Vermont. So even though Hitler is long dead, Bob remains the man of the family. The boy and his father, once so close, are now divided by divorce. Bob gets a letter that ends with the line, "Whenever you care to write to me, I will answer."

To the son, that line is the end of the line.

When still at CKS he joined Troop 20 of the Boy Scouts. He had been a Cub Scout at Lincoln and again in California and Scouting continued to hold great attraction. As a Cub he progressed from Wolf and Bear and Lion and then to the top spot, Webelos. So as a

Boy Scout he aims to be an Eagle, which is as good as it gets. Now he goes from Tenderfoot to Second Class, First Class, Star and Life, even becoming a member of the elite Order of the Arrow, earning all the merit badges required to get that far. He needs twenty-one badges, and certain ones at that, to attain the rank of Eagle. By now, after four years, he's earned twenty of them (the most recent is Rabbit Raising).

He practices Lifesaving, the last required, all summer at Camp Sunrise in Benson and the Troop 20 camp on Lake Bomoseen. On Labor Day he's ready to prove his prowess to a counselor now driving the sixteen miles from Rutland to put him to the test. He's sure he'll ace the exam.

But he won't. Not because fails the exam. He fails to take it at all.

A comely girl paddles up to the Bomoseen camp beach as he practices. She invites him to come into her canoe. He climbs in, paddles away with the kidnapper and leaves the counselor in the lurch on the beach– and fails to take the test.

By the time he apologizes and patches things up with the counselor it's autumn, too cold to swim outdoors. The closest indoor pool lies sixty-eight miles away in Burlington. Unless he can persuade the counselor to take him there.

So he waits.

But that winter the Boy Scout administration changes the requirements, meaning he will have to master six more badges. Meanwhile, his sophomore high school classmates tease him for remaining a Boy Scout at such an advanced age. He caves and abandons the quest for the Eagle badge.

The fallout from this failure is far worse than not winning.

The *Rutland Herald* always runs a photo of an Eagle scout and his mother, the latter wearing a miniature Eagle badge. Because she served as both mother and father in support of his Scouting activities for so many years she makes no secret of her disappointment in her son.

She is badgeless. And unphotographed. And unboastful.

A prime example of such support surrounds a wintertime overnight hike. The troop plans to spend the night in pup tents in Rutland's Cedar Swamp. The forecast calls for below-zero temperatures. His mother flatly opposes the idea. Certainly not. What kind of a mother would let her kid do that? He cannot not go.

That's final, she says.

It isn't.

He whines. He claims every single Scout, all forty of them, will say he's a sissy if he doesn't join them in the snowy cedar swamp. So, against her better judgment, she relents. Thirty-four mothers stand their ground and forbid it. Bob and only five others spend the night, close to a campfire, with occasional short stints of shivering in their sleeping bags. At dawn they fail to fry breakfast eggs. They don't crack.

Almost like the scouts themselves, they are frozen solid.

When he gets home later that morning he affirms to his mother (Oh, sure!) that the entire troop attended. The scoutmaster, however, tells the *Rutland Herald* about the trip and the paper publishes a story the next day, headlined "Six Brave Scouts." The whole community learns that Bob's humiliated mother knows no better than to let her boy sleep in the snow when it is sixteen below.

The last merit badge his mother sews on his sash, although not Life Saving, becomes life altering. He becomes so infatuated with rabbits that other activities remain secondary. He will pursue rabbit raising for another sixty-five years.

He not only earns the rabbit raising badge, years later he will create a new badge manual with new requirements and instructions.

Eighty thousand scouts will use it to earn badges of their own. That manual leads to the writing of seven complete books about rabbits that will sell more than half a million copies in English. One goes into five editions after 60 printings and becomes the all-time best-selling manual on domestic rabbits. Even more sell when translated to several other languages in Europe and South America. They will be read even in Asia and he will be visited for advice by rabbit raisers from as far away as Japan.

Bob realizes that raising rabbits for this badge will leave time to pursue others, because the rabbits do most of the work. The first pair, New Zealand Reds, hook him. He raises far more than he must for the requirements. Production becomes dinners for family and others, as he sells excess to friends and neighbors. He continues to raise them through high school and until he joins the Air Force. His brother Steve then has control of the herd but soon sells them all.

While Bob serves his country he loses more than his rabbits. Brother Steve also appropriates his J. C. Higgins .22 rifle and some other guns, plus his sleeping bag and pup tent—in fact just about all his cherished possessions except for the best one of all, his bamboo fly rod.

Bob bought the rod when he was eleven on the layaway plan at Montgomery Ward for twelve dollars at a dollar a week. Memory of Gramp Jones and a willow branch plus a little brook that feeds Mendon River inspired him to get it. Sixty-five years later he still fishes his favorite deep hole in that brook—with the same rod.

Chapter Seventeen
Teen Time

It's August and Monsignor John M. Kennedy, pastor of Christ the King Church in Rutland, pronounces from his pulpit that parents, under pain of mortal sin, must pay for tuition at parochial school. It's their moral obligation of course. No discussion. So say the other two other Catholic pastors in town. The three Catholic grade schools and high school need no development officers nor colorful brochures.

Fear, the most effective motivator, works as well as it always does. So in September of 1950 Mount St. Joseph Academy classrooms overflow with freshmen. They enroll from eighth grades at Christ the King, St. Peter's and the Immaculate Heart of Mary schools, plus a few from Meldon and surrounding towns, including St. Stanislaus in West Rutland.

To create room at the crowded Mount, the Sisters of St. Joseph send fifty college prep freshmen to classrooms at an erstwhile junior college, earlier an elaborate estate and now their novitiate, a couple of miles away. They call it The Annex. The boys, in one home room, and the girls in another, under the tired eyes of two old teaching nuns, mostly make mischief.

Sister Saint Jerome, a mile away from the supervision of her principal, devotes most of the day to her favorite subjects, Latin and English. Sister Mary James, similarly undetected, takes all the time she can to dispense algebra, her specialty. Nellie Rounds, the basketball coach impersonating a general science teacher, serves up forty-five minutes of welcome respite but scant science.

Separate thirty-minute lunchtimes often last longer and reduce class time. On warm September days the boys leave the lunchroom for the large front lawn behind a high cedar hedge. Stripping to their skivvies, they play tackle football sans trouser grass stains and regard to time.

Sister Mary James approaches, haltingly, one hand covering her eyes. Her other rings a bell as hard as she can.

"Boys, boys," she cries, "it's time to come in now."

The boys have acquired an acute case of deafness.

In mid-November, tired of football and too cold for skimpy attire, the boys burn the cedar hedge, bringing laughter from the girls, howls from the sisters, two fire engines and one police car.

The girls take walks in the woods as long as they like after their earlier lunchtime. Some get "lost" behind the big campus. Sister Jerome can't find them and frets.

The two nuns dispense high marks in their pet subjects (except for deportment) despite meager proficiency. Leaked word of their charges' escapades becomes exaggerated gossip at the Academy, growing even quite lurid in the adjacent convent and of course reaching the parents.

Bob's mother fumes.

Catholic education fumbled.

Having avoided St. John's Prep to attend MSJ with friends, Bob finds himself dispatched by his disgusted mother to Rutland High in the fall. He changes schools for the tenth time in ten years. The eleventh will soon ensue. After three days of whining and pleading his mother wilts and sends her sophomore back to MSJ.

The principal squeezes this year's frosh into the Mount. The big bad college prep kids, including Bob, now sit behind desks in traditional MSJ home rooms. As freshmen guinea pigs, they taught the teachers that the expedient Annex experiment had failed.

Now Bob's grades, always at the top before now, suffer, mostly because he fails to study at night or turn in homework. Not all of them though. He continues to excel in English and gets top marks even when he challenges his teachers. Example: Sister Imelda, formerly the Christ the King principal who got him the St. John's Prep scholarship, asks the class to name their two favorite writers. She's hoping they will list the likes of Shakespeare or Chaucer, but Bob offers "two guys named Smith." They are H. Allen Smith, the humorist, and Red Smith, the sportswriter. In response she accords him higher regard even though she's never read either one. That includes recommending him for acceptance by three colleges of his choice. In years to come, she will become the first president of a new college and ask Bob to write the first ads announcing its opening.

Sister Imelda comes in handy another way as well. Bob has a free period in a sophomore semester and wants to take typing. Hunting and pecking at the Rutland *Herald* won't do for this hopeful journalist, but the nun who used to be his sixth-grade teacher won't let him in the class. That's Sister Julia Marie, she of the arched eyebrow, who knows him too well.

"You can't take typing," she tells him. "This class is for girls who plan to be secretaries. We don't have enough typewriters for anybody else. Besides, you just want to get into the room with a bunch of girls."

So Bob asks Imelda to intercede and she tells the tall nun that this kid wants to be a journalist and needs to know how to touch type. Julia Marie relents and lets him in. While he flubs margins and salutations, he does learn to feel the home keys. She delivers a gift C, saying he'll never qualify as a secretary but she won't damage his overall grade average.

Afternoon supermarket and evening newspaper jobs take most of his spare time which is why he does no homework. His mother needs money and he must remain the man of the family. In addition to his afternoon and evening employment, he tends to his rabbit business, sometimes with schoolmates Joe Romano and Frank Del Mastro as accomplices. His pockets jingle and classmates vote him to the office of treasurer and Most Likely to Succeed. Not so voted, but also successful as rabbit raisers, Joe will become a pastor and Frank a college president.'

Bob does become a writer of some repute however, a debater, and a sometimes thespian, filling roles in several plays, including one opposite the blonde at Vaughan's estate, now a classmate he will call the Breck Girl. He'd like to play baseball, but jobs take precedence. When he writes sports for the *Herald* the nun advising the school paper fires him from his elected position as editor. He fails to lead or write. His head swells. He figures he's too big time for that. His head gets even bigger when the basketball team wins its first state championship and he takes a seat at the press table on the floor of the Boston Garden to cover the school's first game in the New England tournament. He sits between sports writers for the Boston Globe and Associated Press. He will write about it one day only, however. The first game he reports is MSJ's last.

Earlier. a big-time journalism experience occurs at Boys State at Norwich University the summer after his junior year. Bob and classmate friend Mike Halpin are selected to attend the exercise in state government. Both have political ambitions for the week. Both plan stump speeches for high office. Suddenly, laryngitis strikes Bob, leaving him speechless in more ways than one. So instead he applies for and wins the job of editor of the daily newspaper for the delegates. He makes the four-page mimeographed publication into a political pamphlet for his pal. Bob's articles, the epitome of bias, belittle or ignore other candidates.

They get the job done.

Mike wins the governorship handily.

Boys State administrators nearly always send the governor and the newspaper editor to Boys Nation in Washington. Mike boards the bus to D.C. The powers behind Boys State pronounce the newspaper unfairly edited by Bob, who boosted Mike to the gubernatorial victory.

He stays home.

They send the lieutenant governor instead.

High school classes stop thirty minutes before his supermarket job starts. He shoots a few games of pool with pals, eight ball mostly, loser pay (fifteen cents), at John Valente's parlor above the A&P supermarket. He wins or loses little. It takes ten minutes to get there. It's five more before time to punch in at the First National supermarket, only two blocks away.

He does not shoot pool the afternoon of October 3, 1951.The Dodgers play a rubber third game playoff with the Giants. The two teams tie at the end of the regular season and split two playoff tilts. Bob bets his best buddy Sonny Burke a quarter on the outcome, which decides the pennant, before Bobby Thomson hits "the shot heard 'round the world." Baseball fans universally regard it as the most famous homer ever hit. It's a 279-foot can of corn at any ballpark but the horseshoe-shaped Polo Grounds in the Bronx. If plinked at short-sheeted Fenway Park it plops in a glove politely before the Green Monster.

The puny fly ball flops into the left field bleachers as they watch through the window from the sidewalk on the black and white furniture store television set. Devastated, Bob throws two dimes and a nickel into the busy downtown street in front of his longest and best friend ever—since sixth grade.

"There's your twenty-five cents, you son of a bitch," the sore loser screams. "You want it? Go get it!"

Thomson makes him a Giant hater all his life except for a week or so sixty years later.

"It's not nice to hate, Papa," his four-year-old grandson Scott will admonish.

To humor the tot he'll say he will *despise* them instead. That lasts as long as most New Year's resolutions and he goes back to hating in no time. Years earlier, his grown second son, John, meets Thomson at a baseball card and memorabilia show. Exaggerating, the kid tells the ex-Giant, "You ruined my father's life."

Thomson says he's truly sorry about that but still happy he homered.

Fifty years after the horrible hit, a Wall Street Journal reporter writes a happy ending to the story. His tireless and tenacious investigation reveals that Thomson knew what pitch was coming. Giants manager Leo Durocher installed a telescope and an elaborate buzzer system in his Polo Grounds office window in dead center field. His team stole catchers' signs for half the season, flashed them to their hitters and came from thirteen and a half games behind in the middle of August to overtake the Dodgers. There never should even have been a playoff. Long before that revelation, Sonny Burke forgives the sore loser.

Ten years later he ushers at the Dodgers fan's wedding in St. Peter's Church.

Bob's first supermarket job, at independent Boston Market, pays him fifty cents an hour. Pal Jack Slattery also stocks shelves there. The two, only fourteen or fifteen, lack a year or two of qualifying to work in a chain store, required to pay the minimum wage of seventy-five cents. They sometimes make extra money by carrying grocery bags to cars and getting a tip.

They also create some chaos in the produce department.

Carl Brown, the produce manager, often sits on a crate in the walk-in cooler, swigging beer. His special talent is carrying a large cardboard box to the beer cooler, looking both ways to see if owner Joe Tailby is looking, and filching a couple of bottles. He then hides them in his produce cooler. Jack spots this activity. The boys duck into the cooler for a couple of quick swigs.

Brownie walks in on them.

"I will kick your ass if you try this again," he threatens.

The boys command him to keep the cooler well supplied or they will squeal.

Brownie obtains a measure of revenge when he offers Bob a new green pepper. It's so tasty he says, it demands sampling. The gullible boy obliges and takes a big bite. His mouth catches fire. While Brownie laughs, Bob races to the water cooler. The lady who runs the bakery intercepts him before he can drink. Water will only spread the flames, she says, and hands him a dinner roll, which provides relief.

At sixteen Bob applies to the chain supermarket First National, which must pay 75 cents an hour. In a year he advances from stocking shelves to running a cash register and his pay goes up to 95 cents and then $1.10. The hours are 4 to 6 Monday through Thursday, and

4-9 on Fridays. Saturday hours are either 9-6 or half the day. If he has a basketball game to cover for the paper on a Friday night, manager Jim Powers lets him off.

Brisk checkout business makes most of the time fly but Friday nights drag. Late on one of these he whips a glass bottle of ketchup off the counter into a brown grocery bag—except for the perfect circle of glass on the bottom. It seems connected to the stainless-steel counter. Sixteen ounces of sticky sauce sloop across the next three ladies in line. It leaves his face redder than theirs. The store gets away easy though, paying only the dry-cleaning bills.

Another day he cringes at the counter when he drops a sweating and slippery quart soft drink bottle. It breaks and splashes and cuts a woman's nylon stocking and even her ankle. Damages? Only an apology, another bottle and a small bandage. Bob thinks himself pretty lucky.

That luck looks like it's run its course on the warm June night of the senior ball. After the dance, Bob and the Breck girl ride with Jim Fox and his girlfriend to Jim's physician uncle's camp on Lake Sunset, about twenty miles away. The four of them decide to go for a late-night swim. The Breck Girl quickly doffs her dress and dives off the dock, deep into the murky water.

She surfaces screaming, one hand reaching for the starlit sky.

Chapter Eighteen

Dodging a Dead End; Disaster

Oh, no, Bob thinks. I take this date out here swimming and she's drowning. He and Jim jump in, only to find her niftily treading water while nevertheless wailing, one arm in the air. She has forgotten to remove a gift for graduation from her parents—a gold wristwatch.

It drips from the wrist below the hand in the air. Not needing saving, she sidestrokes to shore, weeping all the way. She's convinced the watch is ruined and can think only of the consequences.

Jim says calm down, he's got an idea. He lights the kitchen gas stove oven, hoping to bake the water out of the watch. After threatening to throw cold water on an otherwise warm night, the dehydrated timepiece ticks at the beaming Breck Girl's ear.

So high school days come to a close. Bob's grades are mediocre at best, partly because he studied little and partly because he feared he'd never get to college anyway, so what's the use.

After graduation in June of '54, Bob faces the fact he won't go to college in the fall. He holds letters of acceptance from Seton Hall, Syracuse and Marquette universities. He even becomes an alternate to West Point but the kid ahead of him fails to break a leg or anything else and of course attends.

He leaves the First National, where he cannot get full-time hours. A full-time job awaits at the Montgomery Ward warehouse, assisting the receiving manager. He unloads railroad cars full of kitchen appliances, roofing shingles and furniture with a two-wheeled hand truck. Then he pushes them to a loading dock for possession by customers.

So Bob hauls stoves and refrigerators with a heavy heart.

His classmate pals now attend college. "Most Likely to Succeed?" He thinks not.

He wins a salesclerk spot in the Montgomery Ward retail store. It might lead somewhere, but nowhere he wants to go. Another department store, the Economy, pays a bit better but in a dead-end job. The newspaper has no openings. He fails the Foreign Service exam. He plans to earn enough money for college next fall but that's a pipe dream. What little he makes he gives to his mother and spends on movies with the Breck Girl. She works at a local insurance office, training to be an underwriter. He approaches despair, but she argues he'll find a good career. Right now, at a difficult time, she provides encouragement. One day though, when he clearly sees a way to succeed, it will seem to matter little. She will dump him.

He's subject to the draft, so nobody wants him in a training program. He might as well join the military. If he enlists now, at age eighteen, he will qualify for the Post-Korea G.I. Bill. That will provide tuition money when he gets out. But if he works and waits another year until nineteen, he might qualify for the aviation cadets and become a pilot and officer.

So he works and waits, and the G.I. Bill expires, but he qualifies for the cadets. The Air Force recruiter, selling all the way, says if he enlists first he'll shorten waiting time for the cadet class. That's what he does and agrees to sign up on October 11, after the World Series is over. The Dodgers will be in it, and he wants to watch it on his mother's black and white tv.

As luck would have it, he might miss it and never join the Air Force.

Friday, September 30, 1955, will be remembered as the night young movie star James Dean crashed his Porsche and died. Bob will instead remember it as the night of a trip to Middlebury College and a concert/dance. He and the Breck Girl are to ride in Norwich University sophomore John Mullen's dad's big new Oldsmobile Ninety-eight. High school pal Terry Hannon and his date are also to take the seventy-mile round-trip, along with Mullen's date. The three boys will ride up front: the girls in back.

The day before, the Breck Girl falls and breaks her wrist, so that night they watch television in her living room instead. On the way back from the college John crashes the car into a tree, killing Hannon, sitting in suicide seat.

Bob calls the Breck Girl's injury a lucky break.

Before a week elapses, Bob watches Johnny Podres shut out the Yankees, pitching the Brooklyn Dodgers to their first and only World Series title. That victory will remain indelible in his memory. It leads to a fateful meeting and extraordinary relationship with the hero himself.

Fifty years later.

Chapter Nineteen
In the Air Force

Why, the sergeant-counselor at the air base, Sampson, near Geneva, New York, asks him, does he want to be a pilot.

"Because I'll be an officer and earn more than an enlisted man," he replies with certainty, based on the experience with his army officer father.

"Wrong answer," the sergeant says. "If you don't have a burning desire to fly airplanes, you will wash out of the training in two weeks."

Well, that makes sense and as luck would have it while he ponders the decision, an appealing opportunity presents itself. The base needs a hospital historian, a writer, in the information services career field, which means journalism. In the scant free time basic training provides, he practices his typing by putting dimes into a Royal standard at the base exchange. His mother mails many of his clippings from the *Herald* and Bill Dexter sends that letter of recommendation. He passes a typing test, impresses the major who interviews him and wins the position. He completes basic training, which seems easier than long Boy Scout hikes with heavier backpacks.

The downside: on KP duty he learns to break four eggs simultaneously and never eat them scrambled because a few rotten ones always slip into the pot. He also shovels "solids" out of the septic pool
and into garbage cans. He endures a tetanus shot and can hardly
don his shirt but then must do jumping jacks while his hi-cut bro-
gans create blisters on his heels.

After eleven weeks of basic and a three-day pass to hitchhike
home and back, he reports to the 1,500-bed hospital at Sampson
with one stripe on his sleeve. Instead of a bunk in an open bay, he
gets a two-man room with a lab technician.

WAF Airman Second Class Joanne Cyrus, the current historian, has become pregnant and thus due for imminent discharge. Her
condition, appreciated by Bob, opens the position. Before she leaves,
she shows him the ropes. He reports to the major who hired him.

He begins to interview department heads and examine case
histories, looking for the unusual. He types the hospital story on
AB Dick stencils, mimeographs them and punches the pages for
binding between hard book covers. One copy goes to the Library of
Congress. Others reach the colonel who commands the hospital and
some specialty department heads. He keeps one for the file.

The first six-month edition resembles the many previous semi-
annual reports. But midway through research and interviews for the
second the Air Force decides to reassign all 40,000 troops and shut
down the base and hospital. His subsequent edition chronicles the
demise of the facility in stages, which shrinks from 1,500 beds by
several hundred beds a month to a mere 10-bed dispensary. Bob
doesn't stay at Sampson until he is the last one to turn off the light,
but the place becomes nearly deserted. The remaining jokers say
that by September '56, it went from the largest Air Force hospital to
a Band-Aid.

All that first year at Sampson he hitchhikes home to Rutland on weekends and the occasional three-day pass. His main objective: to see the Breck Girl. He reaches her Rutland doorstep by 9 p.m. or so on Friday, stays an hour and thumbs the seven miles home to Mendon. They usually see a movie at the Paramount on Saturday. Sunday afternoon he hitchhikes the three hundred miles back to the base.

A uniformed airman's thumb is a ticket for a swift trip but one goes faster than the others. He shudders in a Jaguar roadster at a hundred and three miles an hour on the New York Thruway painted with patches of ice. If we ever hit one, he feels, we will fly as high as an Air Force fighter.

On a much calmer day he climbs into the back seat of a car driven by an elderly man. The driver and his wife remain mute for a few miles. Then the woman asks, "Where did your bus break down, sonny?" She has mistaken his dress blues for the togs of a Greyhound bus driver.

After a thirty-day furlough that fall he leaves home for the base in Cheyenne, F.E. Warren, originally a cavalry post. He hoped for one closer to home, but the order assigns him to a new base paper, the *Skyliner*.

He takes the trip by sharing the driving and the gas with another airman going to the western base. First he hitchhikes to Rochester, New York, to meet him. They reach a cheap hotel in Cleveland that night, the Palmer house in Chicago the next. Then they endure a long and boring drive through Iowa and Nebraska cornfields, overnight in Omaha and to Cheyenne the middle of the next day.

He meets the *Skyliner* editor, his first Mormon. Gary Blodgett also writes sports part-time for the morning *Wyoming Eagle*, mostly the exploits of the teams of the public and parochial high schools.

Bob and Gary hit it off immediately but don't share a beer in the barracks. Gary doesn't even drink a Coke or coffee—no alcohol and no caffeine. When in two months Gary receives his discharge, he drives home to report for the *Deseret News* in Utah, which he will do for fifty years. Before he leaves he recommends Bob for his job at the *Eagle*. Simultaneously, the officer in charge, Captain LaCroix, promotes Bob to editor of the *Skyliner* over a staff of four. Bob wins a second stripe and a higher proficiency rating which lets him supervise an airman with three and even a tech sergeant. Things are looking up.

But they are about to change.

The Cheyenne air takes his breath away. Thinner than the atmosphere in Denver, the high plains cowtown surpasses the altitude of the mile-high city. That's an advantage when the fast-breaking basketball team plays host to one from anywhere closer to sea level. But for Bob it causes a couple of problems, one a near catastrophe.

On a frigid January Sunday morning, he stamps his freezing cold feet outside the multi-denominational chapel, waiting for the Protestants to exit. Once inside the stuffy building for Mass, still wearing his wool Melton military overcoat, he faints and falls between the pews, out cold from the sudden heat. A couple of buddies pick him up and lug him over to the barracks. By the time they park him on his bunk he's fine.

After leaving the downtown office of the *Eagle* about ten on a hot and humid summer night, he waits at a corner for the local bus back to the base. As it slows to stop, he will feel woozy again, try to latch onto a light post for support but slump into the street. The bus driver brakes just in time. Again, a couple of G.I.s pick him up and prop him upright on a seat near the door. He wears a sheepish grin.

"Just another drunken airman in the gutter," the driver announces to his passengers. "Nothing to worry about."

These are the only times he ever faints. But the next day, he nearly keels over again.

Chapter Twenty

Two Rejections

The pink envelope looks just like the ones the Breck Girl sends every couple of days. She's the girl he's been nuts about for nearly four years now. The girl who acted opposite him in the senior play and shared graduation festivities. The girl who inspired him because she attended Mass every morning. The one who gave him her high school portrait with the inscription, "I will never forget you no matter what but I hope what never happens."

Right in his two hands "what" just happened.

The proverbial *Dear John* letter that's what.

She hoped to let him down easy.

"I don't want to hurt you."

She does.

Well, he thinks, what do you expect? You are two thousand miles away and won't be back again for a year or more. She'll be twenty-one this fall. Do you think she wants to wait around until who knows when to welcome somebody still helping support his mother?

Somebody with no money, no car and no prospects for much of anything? And while her girlfriends marry monthly, one after another?

Probably worse, in the mind of her mother: he's neither Irish nor French, as her parents.

Get real, he rationalizes. Get on with it. It's just another rejection. His father. His grandfather. Even his Godfather. If rejection makes you tough, he is a military mess hall steak. His skin is as thick as an Irish brogue straight from the "ould sod."

He doesn't know it now, but rejections will one day help make him a rousing success in sales because he won't take no for an answer.

No money? Actually, right now he does pocket a little dough. He earns more than his military paycheck at the *Eagle*. Local sports require coverage all year, even those events he had never imagined. Such as Frontier Days—the rodeo. Dick White, the sports editor, directs him to report daily on calf roping, bull riding and bronco busting at the week-long "Daddy of 'Em All." Surprised, Bob replies that as an easterner, he has never even seen a rodeo (oh, except for a phony one in Madison Square Garden when he was only five).

"You signed on here as a sportswriter," Dick says, "and rodeo stands as our biggest sport."

With that, he walks down to Western Ranchman Outfitters and buys a cowboy hat and boots. At the rodeo, he looks the part as he plants his Wranglers on the fence rail with a notepad and pencil. Except during the raucous chuck wagon races, when he must stay way back or make some of the news himself as the horses and wagons careen around the dirt track, sometimes crashing and even depositing riders on the enclosure.

Newspaper pay, a pittance then (and even much later), nevertheless pads the pocket of the two-stripe airman. Half his Air Force money ($40) goes home to his mother in the form of an allotment. So when pay call falls at eight o'clock on a Saturday morning, a day when he doesn't report for duty at the *Skyliner* office, he rolls over in his bunk. He can pick up his paycheck later. Besides, he's been at the Eagle until after the 10 p.m. sports deadline, and then in a bar with Dick for a couple of beers to unwind before boarding the late bus back to the base.

Ditching pay call earns a discrepancy report. Consequences usually mean cleaning the latrine for a week. Sacking in on a Saturday makes it worth it. He gets very good at latrine duty anyway. But skipping payday formation does not introduce him to his first toilet brushes.

What does? A fright in the middle of the night.

Sound asleep in the old brick barracks open bay fitted out with twenty-four double bunks, he thinks he's dreaming and reaches for something warm and furry on his head. It's an absolute nightmare and he bolts upright from his bottom bunk so suddenly he bumps his head on a steel bar supporting the springs above. He screams and startles the boys in their bunks, then drags a blanket downstairs to the day room. He spends the rest of the night prone on a pool table.

No way is he going back to that bunk in the bay.

The next day he buys forty-eight wood and wire mousetraps, makes the "midnight requisition" of a jar of peanut butter from the mess hall on the first floor, baits the traps and sets one below each of the forty-eight vertical steel lockers. Then he draws up a chart on poster board, a sort of score sheet, numbering each locker and trap. He tapes it to the wall behind his bunk. He sketches a Mickey Mouse head and ears silhouette for each time the traps snap. For three lovely nights they snap, snap, snap successfully under the lockers. For three days he drops executed mice down the johns and draws Mickeys. He tells these ground force guys that five dead mice will make them an Air Force fighter pilot ace.

Fifty mice or more later, with word of the contest, the first sergeant scoops up the traps, removes the scoreboard and brings in a
civilian company exterminator. He duly sentences the mouse mur-
derer to a week of latrine duty. The first sarge, trying to sound serious, says Bob should have reported the mouse incident, not taken
the situation into his own traps. Of course, none of the other residents of the barracks, vying with each other for rodent air superior-
ity, had reported it either.

Okay, some non-ace snitched.

Cheyenne has big snowstorms. You aren't allowed to leave the
base in winter without blankets, shovels and emergency food. Staying on the base during a big one means "confinement" to the barracks. Ropes link some buildings so nobody will get lost in a bliz-
zard if he ventures out. The lifelines don't reach all duty stations
but they do join the barracks to the Airmen's Club so beer can be
brought back for a day of card playing, Ping Pong and pool.

While the first sergeant expresses little love for the barracks
mouse king, Captain LaCroix becomes so enamored with his editing work that he picks Bob for plum temporary duty in Houston to
help cover a navigation training meet. The task is to put out a daily
newsletter, persuade the *Houston Chronicle* to cover the event and
write hometown news releases. He also writes a recap feature published in the *Air Force Times*.

It's a ten-day trip, with a weekend off. His father, still a career
Army officer, is stationed at Fort Hood just fifty miles away. He decides to phone him. It's the first time they have spoken since he was
eleven. That was ten years ago on Mendon Mountain.

Texas, Bob thinks, might be the last place they ever meet again.

"I'll drive down there on Saturday when we're both off duty," his
father says. "Then how about we'll go to Galveston for a shore dinner?"

The lieutenant colonel in civies shows up at Ellington Air Force Base in a shiny '59 Ford Skyliner, a convertible with a retractable steel top. The airman second class climbs in.

Conversation is uncomfortable. Neither wants to dig into the past, and so, as if they had met and chatted every day of the week, talk ranges around current events. His father, still a special services officer, directs physical training and athletics at the fort. He asks about Air Force duty, but nothing about things at home. He never mentions his former wife, and little about their other two sons.

They both look out a restaurant window at Galveston Bay and discuss the fortunes of the Dodgers. When the dinner check arrives, his dad matter-of-factly stuns him

"Let's go Dutch."

They split the bill.

Back at the Houston barracks, they shake hands. That's that, and his dad drives off.

"Let's go Dutch," Bob mutters. "Let's go Dutch." This from the high-ranking officer to the lowly enlisted man. This from the father who failed to support his children, let alone take care of their mother.

Bob doesn't care if he ever sees him again.

He never will.

Chapter Twenty

Back East and the Far East

Back in Cheyenne, the editor on the air base chooses the articles for the paper. He covers the choice assignments himself, including an interview and even a chance to dance with the movie star Terry Moore at the Airmen's Club. Watching basketball and baseball games with a scorebook here and away also makes serving his country passable if not totally enjoyable.

Bob's favorite games take place in Denver against both Lowry Air Force Base and Fort Carson Army teams. The Warren team includes both enlisted men and officers. Traveling, they wear civilian clothes, sport coats and ties and slacks. They enjoy training table steaks in the officers' mess at Lowry with Air Force Academy cadets before their move to the Colorado Springs campus, still under construction. They also get extra money for restaurant meals. Rank means nothing on the road. It's almost like being a civilian again.

At the *Eagle*, not only does he write sports, he subs for the vacationing columnist who regularly responds to troubled readers. For two weeks Bob doles out advice to the lovelorn, with the pseudonym "Susan Summers.".

He also mails clippings home to the Breck Girl, hoping she will see the error of her ways. For her birthday, he wires flowers. She promptly sends a thank you note, cordial but non-committal:

"Thank you for the lovely flowers. I don't know why you would send them."

She knows why of course. He hopes she will see him again. He'll have a chance. The following fall he gets orders for the Far East. With a thirty-day leave, he has time at first to head for home.

He has plenty of *time* to go home but military travel pay covers only a flight from Cheyenne straight to San Francisco, the port of debarkation, leaving no funds to fly in the other direction. Extra money earned at the *Eagle* buys a coach train ticket east. He sits and slumps in a club car chair for seventy-two hours, downing sandwiches, drinking beer, dozing and dreaming of the Pullman berths of his boyhood.

Yes, the Breck Girl will see him at her home, up the stairs of the carriage house behind the Vaughn mansion they had explored years before. He stands on the stone step and rings the bell, hoping she will call to him to come up.

As she had so many times.

Not this time.

She meets him down at the storm door.

She smiles amiably but coolly. She's uncomfortable. It's over. He doesn't ask her why; he thinks he really knows. She never volunteers a reason. They wish each other well. With a handshake, they part for what he figures is forever. He walks home to his mother's. For a couple of weeks, he mopes around the house. His high school pals are nowhere to be found because of college or the military. He takes a bus to New York and a plane at LaGuardia for San Francisco.

The assignment: Pacific Area Command Air Force headquarters in Korea, Osan Air Base, on the staff of the newspaper that serves all the airmen in the Land of the Morning Calm. The Flying Tiger Airlines Super Constellation, four-engine and propeller-driven, lifts off from Travis Air Force Base, not far from San Francisco. First stop, for a several hours of service and refueling: Honolulu. Delightedly, he samples fresh pineapple, right off the bush. Sadly, he sees several bikinied twenty-somethings squired by sugar daddies on Waikiki beach.

Long hours later the big plane lands beside a lagoon at tiny Wake Island, again for more fuel. The rusted hull of a WWII Japanese ship provides the only sight to see.

From there they leave on the second to last leg—to Haneda Airport, otherwise known as TIA, Tokyo International Airport. Walking through the terminal Bob thinks he could be on the other side of the moon. It's different here. Everybody is different. Everything is different—exotically so. A waiting military bus takes him to the Yamato air base. After a night there mostly staring at a strange seaweed tile ceiling, Bob boards a C-124 Globemaster at Tachikawa air base. It's a huge, four-engine cargo plane with clamshell doors, nicknamed "Big Shaky." A four-hour flight on a steel seat over the Sea of Japan and several smoking volcanoes takes him to Kimpo airfield, which serves as the Seoul International Airport. Desolate and forlorn Kimpo, seemingly still war-torn, has but a single hanger. It holds soldiers' bodies still hanging inside four years after the armistice because it's thought to be booby trapped.

The back of a weapons carrier, a cross between a Jeep and a pickup truck, then bounces him thirty-five miles in three more hours to Osan. First it bumps over Han River rocks that serve as a bridge out of Seoul. Then it rumbles over the rutted dirt road they call the Seoul-Pusan Highway.

A corrugated galvanized steel Quonset hut awaits as his quarters for the next year. No custom abode, this barracks building, looking like a tin can split lengthwise, is one of 170,000 manufactured since World War II. Shipped from the states, it sits amid several similar structures on a concrete slab. It's reached by pierced steel planking, known locally as PSP, which lifts men out of the mud, but can't keep simultaneous dust out of their eyes. That seemingly contradictory combination results from complete erosion of the mountainsides. Warplane bombs burned every tree. Rains sloshed mud to the valleys. Subsequent wind sent dust down from the summits. It also brought the stench of farmers' honey buckets and their rice paddies.

Now he recalls his father's assignment there after WWII. He supervised tree planting, required because the occupying Japanese clear-cut the hills for lumber. The fires of the Korean conflict that killed those trees led to the law that decreed anyone caught wielding an ax or saw on those hills would earn capital punishment.

Before the houseboy settles him into his bunk and locker in the open bay, before he faces down a big rat on the PSP that leads to the latrine hut, and even before he reports to the newspaper office, he makes up his mind to get out of here long before the end of his tour of duty. He doesn't know how, but he just knows he must. Let's face it, this place stinks—even indoors where jet fuel-fired stoves heat his hut and office. He will learn that the only way to avoid all the stench of camp and countryside is to go up in a 'copter and open the window.

As a reporter for the weekly *Sabre Star*, he writes news and features for all of the Air Force in Korea. He works in an office inside headquarters of the 314th Air Division, a linked group of Quonset huts sitting on concrete. High on a hill, it overlooks surrounding rice paddies, farmers' thatched mud houses, huts mostly, and the flight line where a pair of F-86 Sabre jets scramble from the PSP runway every three minutes. One can also see the tiny ramshackle village of Osan, known to the airmen, who rarely venture outside the airbase gates, as the "V". The people there are pathetically poor. They have no automobiles, but travel to nearby towns on so-called Kimchi buses, made from parts of military vehicles stolen by "slicky boys" and owned by Syngman Rhee, the president of the Republic of (South) Korea.

The paper needs two editors in chief because not one print shop in Korea can handle a job in English. Each week one editor supervises a staff of six writers, a photographer, and a pretty, young Korean secretary named Kim Chin Sook. Except for the cleaning lady, an old mamasan as they call her, Kim is the only woman in the headquarters complex. Once in a while a female American military nurse appears, but not for long. No WAFs or military dependents may stay in Korea.

Then the editor flies with copy and layout to Tokyo to be typeset, proofread and printed during the following week. The editor oversees those operations, some of them tricky because the Japanese typesetters know only as much English as he knows Japanese—which isn't much.

At the Linotype machine, the operator merely matches symbol for symbol, not knowing how to read what he's typing. A comment that's all too common when proofreading is when the editor says "Sayonara that line (or letter) papasan." He might go so far as to say *taipu* or *insatu shimasu* (type it or print it) for the finished copies, to be distributed to Air Force installations up and down the peninsula, from Seoul to Pusan. Meanwhile, his counterpart, back at the base, controls the writing, photography and layout of the following week's issue, then takes the copy to Tokyo before the other guy gets back.

They rarely see each other and only imagine friendly waves from the windows of Gooney Birds or Globemasters as they pass each other over the Sea of Japan. Occasionally they catch a hop in a T-33 Trainer or TF-86 Sabre jet, cutting the travel time from four to two hours.

The job is definitely the dream of everybody on the staff. Why not, it means per diem cash, every other week in a hotel, eating in exotic restaurants and comfortably living the nightlife in an exciting city, compared to the stinking slogging in mud and dust, slush and snow.

Bob determines to succeed one of these editors, and in two months one completes his tour. Bob's *Skyliner* editing credentials earn a bi-weekly ticket to Tokyo. Every other week he leaves the Quonset hut, the unheated latrine and the mess hall with its powdered eggs, powdered milk and bread baked with so little shortening it crumbles in his hands.

He also leaves guard duty on the flight line– four hours on and four off, twenty-four a day for two weeks, punctuated by the occasional tracer bullets fired in the night by Commie saboteurs from the north.

The Tokyo deal includes chauffeured transportation around the city in a Mercedes sedan, courtesy of Mr. Otake, the print shop owner who cultivates and caters to editors who are a nice slice of his bread and butter. The printer buys lunches and hosts Bob for dinners on tatamis in fancy traditional Japanese restaurants, complete with Geisha girls at his elbow. A favorite fling afterward features three nightclub floor shows and two drinks, with a cab ride in between, for the equivalent of two dollars. The cherry on top: sleeping late, room service in the morning and sightseeing, including ancient shrines. What's more, he wears civies because regulations forbid Air Force personnel to be in uniform. The Japanese still see reminders, destroyed buildings and subway stations, of bombing attacks some twelve years earlier.

That's the upside. It gets him out of Korea, but the week back there and all that goes with it is the schizophrenic downside. Focusing on the job keeps him reasonably sane. That includes interviewing Bob Hope and Jayne Mansfield on the plane from Tokyo, during which Hope nearly ejects himself from the co-o pilot seat.

Bob photographs the blonde bombshell at the airplane door when it opens at Osan. Because he's on the tarmac and she's at the top of the stairway, his twin lens reflex gives him an image of a headless Mansfield even though it includes the sky above. There are two big round reasons why she seems decapitated years before it actually happens in a convertible in America.

He also presents a Korean papasan hat to Hedda Hopper and, meets Cardinal Spellman, while fending off a captain in the office who doesn't understand that he's an executive pencil pusher instead of an enlisted journalist.

More mundane events include drinking twenty-five cent martinis and ten-cent beers at the airmen's club, plus teaching the touring Kim Sisters to eat spaghetti by swapping chop sticks for a fork and spoon to twirl the strands, just as Bob Wilson had taught him back in the days he greeted customers at the Rutland music store. He's so impressed with them he writes a feature for the paper. It gets picked up by *Pacific Stars & Stripes,* the daily for all the military personnel in Asia, and then in the *Air Force Times. Time* magazine runs a story with their photos.

The next thing Bob knows, the sisters are in Las Vegas as part of a *China Doll Revue.* Then they become a feature of the wildly popular Ed Sullivan (television) Show.

Bob thinks he has an eye for talent.

As for the beer at the club, one brand claims the dubious title of the worst in America. Each month a shipment of suds arrives at the club. It includes national brands but also local ones so that, supposedly, a G.I. can swig his favorite malt beverage as if he's in his neighborhood gin mill at home. Instead, everybody samples everybody else's local suds. Cases of only one American brand remain in the cooler at the end of the month. Nobody will swallow a second bottle of it. If ever there was a beer test market this is it. The airmen pronounce it the worst beer brand. (In the interest of full disclosure, a Korean brand sits in the cooler with it. It's called Oriental Beer or O.B. The airmen call it B.O. They say it's brewed with Seoul City sewer water even though Seoul has no sewers—water of all kinds runs through the streets.)

Twenty years later Bob will find validation of that verdict when he travels in San Francisco. He drives by the brewery that sold the stuff. It's an abandoned building—Lucky Lager went beer belly up— somehow surviving ten years beyond the Osan verdict.

All in all, a week in and a week out of Korea beats staying there all the time, but his main objective is to get out permanently before his year-long duty tour ends. He finally gains that goal when selected to become a features writer and rewrite editor in Tokyo for *Stars & Stripes.*

Chapter Twenty-one
More Time in Tokyo

Civilian editors run *Stripes*, mostly because military reporter types leave regularly for the states. The paper requires continuity. Everyone, civilians and G.I.s, are top-notch newsmen, including excellent photographers and cartoonists. Some of the civilians, former military, simply love staying in Tokyo. Others continue journalism careers in the states. Many celebrated newsmen are as much veterans of *Stripes* as they are of their military service. Rubbing elbows with them adds to Bob's journalism education and embellishes his resume for civilian life. The list of former staffers looks like a who's who of journalism.

And now he could be one of them.

The position includes per diem, which puts money in his pocket. He makes the yen and scrip yield more by tipping the charge of quarters at nearby Hardy Barracks a buck a night for the bunk of another G.I., doubtless shacked up with some josan doll elsewhere in Tokyo. Another dollar will deliver the absentee's mess card for the dining hall with linen tablecloths and China dishes instead of Osan tin trays. A menu and Japanese girls serving terrific food come with it. So on twelve dollars a day, supposedly for hotels and restaurants, he retains ten bucks to blow on night clubs and shopping. Plenty of time remains for it because he works only afternoons and evenings at the morning paper, giving him late nights off (and late sleep in the mornings).

Some Japanese nationals also work at *Stripes* and one secretary takes a shine to him and asks him to take her to an American movie at a nearby theater. It's *Run Silent, Run Deep*, made from a book about the U.S. Navy Submarine Service blowing up Japanese ships. Bob read the book in high school and knows that torpedoes will blast Nip sailors into the air and overboard hollering banzai. Uneasy, Bob doesn't want to be the only American in a theater full of countrymen watching hundreds of Japanese killed on the screen. He nudges the girl near the climax and takes her by the arm.

They exit the theater hastily before it's too late and the lights go up.

In English she wants to know why. He says he will explain later.

Instead, he buys her an ice cream cone and walks her home. About the same age, they swap stories about their childhood in the war. He bought savings stamps at school for war bonds and collected bales of newspapers. With bamboo spears, she practiced attacking invading American soldiers.

A dollar is good for three hundred sixty yen, and only ten yen, about two point eight cents, buys an ice cream cone or a ride on the subway. So everything is relatively cheap and he is really flush. One purchase is at Takashimaya's, a big department store, for a pair of its renowned pearl earrings, which he sends to the Breck Girl (who refuses them and gives them to his mother).

Another expenditure: a couple of cameras. He buys a Nikon S, a top-notch thirty-five-millimeter rangefinder model. He buys a Ricohflex twin lens reflex, has a problem with it jamming, takes it into the Riken factory and gets it fixed on the spot for free. Another purchase, a Yashica mat, also a TLR, further equips him to practice advanced picture taking in the Far East. That camera produces a surprise picture of Bob and Hirohito together. The emperor rides by in his maroon Rolls Royce and Bob captures a shot of him in the back seat from the curb. When he develops the film, he sees himself reflected in the shiny rear door as the emperor stares out at the street.

But like real jobs, the dream job inevitably concludes.

First though, he flies in helicopters all over Korea. He writes features, including profiles of the Korean air force and naval academies. The latter assignment's not bad, because it takes him to Chin Hae on the southwest tip of the peninsula, untouched by war. He thinks it amazing how beautiful a place in Korea can be. The worst assignment takes him on "The Night Train to Pusan." For that he boards a nearly empty car in Seoul, rides all night on a hard wood bench and watches a Republic of Korea army MP throw a stowaway fellow ROK soldier off the train to his death. Bob disembarks at the southern city, which is a complete mess. Strewn with the "households" of the desperately poor, the streets include one mother and two toddlers on a piece of cardboard on the trolley tracks. When the trolley comes near, she slides cardboard, pots and pans and dishes and blankets off the tracks.

The "rich" people live in tunnels and under bridges.

Then, a couple of months before his tour supposedly will end, he goes back to his Quonset hut and newspaper at Osan. As one of the editors again, he stays here and goes to Tokyo every other week once more.

He buys canned fish and meat and boxed crackers in Tokyo to take back for his week at Osan. He lives on a lot of it at Osan because he can't stand what the mess hall offers, having become used to high living in Tokyo. He also buys cases of sodium glutamate called Aji-nomoto to fence to the Korean houseboy, which means more spending money. Koreans also want to buy scissors, which he smuggles and sells at triple what they cost him. Even though he smokes a pack of Camels a day he can fence a carton or two a week. The houseboy pays five bucks for a carton that cost only $1.10. Kim Won Chul turns them over in the "V," for ten dollars.

According to the much-studied calendar, the year-long overseas assignment finally draws to a close and he will return stateside in time for Christmas in Vermont.

Not.

Matsu and Quemoy, islands off China, get shelled from the mainland, so he's "frozen" during this so-called crisis for about a month before the geniuses in charge realize that journalists are "soft core" or not essential to any kind of potential combat. They thaw him out for reassignment to the Z.I.

His next duty station will be Dobbins Air Force Base in Marietta, Georgia, a suburb of Atlanta, where he will edit the base newspaper.

The day finally arrives when he's supposed to fly home, but Korea won't release him gracefully.

Chapter Twenty-two
Far East to Southeast

He boards a Globemaster at Osan for the trip to Tachikawa in Tokyo, the first leg of the long journey home. Everyone calls the clamshell-door aircraft "Old Shaky" because it rumbles and shudders on takeoff. It's history includes a fatal crash a few years earlier. It dropped into the Sea of Japan, drowning all one hundred twenty-nine aboard. Bob knows the aircraft too well, having crisscrossed the sea between Korea and Japan many times this year. The plane persists with its lousy engines' penchant for failing, the pilot feathering one or even two of the four well into the flight. A couple of times the pilot reversed course before reaching the point of no return. It seems almost routine.

Nevertheless, he is not prepared for what happens next.

Immediately the captain announces that the craft and its full load of four hundred men will attempt to return to the runway it left moments earlier. On takeoff the pilot does not merely feather an engine, he really loses one. With a full load, he needs them all on takeoff. But he doesn't have them all.

One falls off and lands in a rice paddy.

Bob looks down out the window and realizes the seriousness of the situation when he sees fire engines spreading foam on the runway.

That's when he produces his "airplane prayer." It goes like this: you look down at the fire engines and you say, "Holy shit." Then you roll your eyes up to the overhead rack and pronounce very piously, "Hail Mary." You do this three times and the plane lands safely and everybody gets out. Some kneel and kiss the pierced steel planking.

Bob's not going home today.

Having sent his mattress and blankets to Supply, he spends the night on his bunk with his overcoat spread on the springs. The next day the Globemaster, equipped with another engine, warms for takeoff and Bob is hot to get aboard and get away. But a bunch of the guys won't bet on the same plane. Not disciplined for refusing orders to reboard, they decide to stay another day for another flight.

But after thirteen months over here Bob might board a box kite. The plane takes him to Tachikawa.

The Super Connie will depart from Haneda the next day, so he decides to visit Mr. Otake at the print shop. That gets him served a sayonara dinner complete with Geisha attendants, but it loses him his Nikon camera, swiped from his locker by the Tachikawa charge of quarters sergeant. Months later he learns the sarge stole a lot of other things, got court martialed and jailed before being dishonorably discharged. None of that can get him his camera back.

The Flying Tiger Super Constellation plane taking him back home drops at the regular stops for refueling at Wake Island and Honolulu. He stays several hours in Hawaii again, and he downs a dish of fresh pineapple, recalling his first one over a year ago. It's so tasty he vows never to eat any other ever again unless he's in Hawaii. Down at Waikiki beach, he becomes depressed again to see hundreds of gorgeous young "round-eyed josans" in the company of old Caucasian men, just as thirteen months before. But if he remembers nothing else at all about the eighteen-hour trip, it's when stewardesses keep waking him up and telling him it is time for breakfast. Again. And again. It has to do with multiple time zones and the international dateline.

Once again at Travis, near Camp Stoneman in Pittsburg, where his father was stationed a dozen years before, he boards a bus to San Francisco for a flight to Boston. Then a bus takes him back to Rutland. The first thing he does is sack out for about fifteen hours, having traveled for thirty-six.

The second thing he does is call the Breck Girl.

The funny thing is his mother had sent him pictures from Christmas time at his house, with the Breck Girl in attendance. Why?

Chapter Twenty-three
Going South

The Breck Girl likes his mother, and wants to cheer her up for Christmas, but it means nothing in his case. No, she won't go out with him. Absence does nothing fonder for her heart as far as he is concerned. So he boards a bus to Atlanta. The first leg is New York and when he transfers from the Vermont Transit to a Greyhound to continue south, it's almost empty. So he seeks out the back seat, which stretches the width of the bus. He sleeps pretty soundly even though the noisy diesel engine behind the seat produces a headache like those from dozing on Globemasters. In Washington the driver rouses him and requires a move up front. They will be crossing the Mason-Dixon line, the driver explains, and down there "The back of the bus is reserved for the colored. It's the law."

Who, Bob wonders, suffers discrimination? What about a tired white G.I. on a thousand-mile trip to a duty station?

So he sits up front and watches out the window as the southland goes by. In North Carolina he sees shacks so shabby that he can look right through the boards front and rear to the backyard. Poverty seems worse than some he saw in war-torn South Korea. He wonders what Atlanta and Dobbins have in store. But even though he has left home again, now in November, he smiles, thinking that by next October he will be free again, at the end of four years in the Air Force. And he makes up his mind that he will never join anything ever again.

He won't even sign up for a library card.

He has traveled a lot. He has lived in a lot of places. He has met a lot of different people. Japanese and Korean guys. Catholics, Protestants, Mormons, city slickers and rednecks, Hispanics called wetbacks and Negroes called colored. He has lived with everybody in every kind of quarters. But here is a surprise for his first time in the south. It's not just a *room* instead of an open bay, or even one with a bathroom complete with a shower, albeit shared with the room next door.

No, the looks of his roommates startle the new editor of the *Dobbins Flyer*.

The black guys, much older than their new roommate, are both career mess hall cooks. And they are fastidious—I mean gung-ho clean. When Bob taps a cigarette ash into a tray they run it into the bathroom and wash it. They don't just empty the trash; they wash out the wastebasket every morning. They sweep and scrub the asphalt tile floor. Bob leaves a magazine on his bunk and they slide it under his pillow.

They may be black, but all he sees is *white*. They wear whites in the kitchen. They wear a path between the barracks and the laundry, bringing back hefty hangers of starched white coats and trousers.

They don't say much. He can't really get a conversation going with them. But they bring back to the barracks room plenty of roast beef, ham, cold cuts, cheese and loaves of fresh baked bread. Bob buys mustard and pickles at the base exchange for the contraband comestibles. They are the best barracks mates ever, despite some late-night drunken escapades. No arguments, they just keep it clean and keep him pampered with plenty of midnight snacks.

Having already seen most of the rest of the country and some outside it, Bob seems a sophisticate in some ways, but the southland holds surprises. Much of it has to do with food. This Friday night he takes the bus to Atlanta, to check out some clubs and take in a movie, but first he stops at a Woolworth's lunch counter. Catholics can't eat meat on Fridays. So he orders a cheese sandwich.

"You want *mineyes* on that? asks the waitress, holding up a jar of mayonnaise.

"No thanks," he tells her. "How about some mustard instead?"

The sandwich arrives and he takes a bite. It oozes mayonnaise.

"I thought we agreed, no mayonnaise; mustard instead."

"I know," she says, "but I put *mineyes* on it anyway. That's the trouble with you damn Yankees. You just don't know how to eat."

Something else the Catholic doesn't know he learns at the movie. Before the feature begins, the newsreel starts. First, the Pope is seen in a procession. Next, the Notre Dame football team scores a touchdown. That brings a surprising whisper from behind him: "Boy, the bead rattlers and mackerel smackers are really in the news tonight!"

On Monday the civilian owner of the print shop for the *Dobbins Flyer* takes him to lunch in Atlanta. It's shortly after President Eisenhower integrates buses and restaurants. A large black woman sits down at a table nearby. She studies the menu. And frowns.

"Do you have chitlins and collard greens?" she asks the waitress.

"No ma'am, we don't.".

"Well pardon me, how about hog jowls and black-eyed peas?"

Same answer, "Sorry ma'am, we don't."

So the woman gets up, slaps down the menu, and storms to the door, stopping there to turn and announce loudly, "That's the trouble with you white folks, you just ain't ready for integration."

Another time, at an Atlanta lunch counter, he orders a roast beef tongue sandwich on rye with raw onion and mustard, something he learned to love way back as a boy in New Jersey.

"How can you eat that?" asks a woman who leans in his direction from a couple of stools down. "It comes right out of the animal's mouth!"

"I never thought much about it," Bob replies. "What are you having?"

"Oh, an egg salad sandwich."

There is some fabulous southern food down here though, and the best of it comes at breakfast in Mississippi at the home of grandparents of a co-worker on the *Flyer*, who invites him to visit for a weekend of squirrel hunting and home cooking.

On this Friday night they walk up stately wide steps to the weathered clapboard farmhouse, part of a plantation in earlier days. Bob soon sits on a stool before a glowing fireplace with the grandfather, who is full of questions and comments certain to skewer the visitor from the north.

"You must know," the old man tells him, "Damnyankee is just one word."

After a chilly night sunk deep in a cozy feather bed, he wakes to a wonderful aroma from downstairs in the dining room. The grandmother serves up a breakfast spread of pancakes, scrambled eggs, grits, thick baked pork chops with applesauce, fried potatoes with gravy, plus coffee with chicory and a huge pitcher of thick, ice-cold buttermilk. For someone eating most of his meals on tin trays in a mess hall for the past three years, this is a breakfast for the ages.

Back in Marietta and Atlanta he avoids the mayonnaise, but not the Southern Bell Telephone Company. A bustling oasis in a desert of rednecks, Atlanta attracts hundreds of true southern belles to the phone company. At 5 p.m. when the day shift ends, scores of operators stream out the front door to face an equal number of airmen—and soldiers too, from Fort McPherson in town. Bob goes to a couple of movies with one redhead. He takes her to Hank and Jerry's Hideaway for Dixieland jazz, and to Georgia Tech hangouts—the Wit's End improv club and the Varsity hamburger joint with servers who sit on car fenders. Although a few dates are all there is between them she phones him repeatedly at the *Flyer* office.

Dobbins trains reservists, known by the permanent party airmen as weekend warriors. It includes Air Force Plant Number Ten, a Lockheed operation modifying B47 bombers into drones. The reservists arrive on Friday nights, in time for chow. Saturday mornings they are first in line for chow at breakfast time. Then they report to duty stations for briefings and classroom sessions, which last until, yup, time for chow. Physical training follows in the guise of baseball, flag football or basketball before ample free time for afternoon shopping in the base exchange—and before time for chow. Saturday night movies, the pool hall, bowling and trips to Atlanta bars don't keep them up too late because if they oversleep on Sunday they will miss chow.

On this Saturday night the pool hall wins a celebrity visitor, Willie Mosconi, the most famous pool player in the country. Bob goes to see him perform and when Mosconi asks for someone to oppose him in a game of straight, Bob volunteers. Mosconi breaks, runs the table, breaks and runs the table again—and then again, while Bob looks on, meekly holding a cue stick, never getting a shot.

After breakfast the reservists piously become religious and pack the chapels before coffee with the *Atlanta Journal* sports and comics sections. Then they pack up and check out of the barracks just before Sunday dinner chow, after which they depart for home, having fulfilled their training assignment and accumulating points toward a pension.

As a permanent party airman and one now with plenty of experience in his career field, Bob edits the weekly base paper, the *Flyer*. While he has not been promoted above airman second class, he does qualify as a senior journalist and supervises a staff of four. If there had been any additional stripes available he would have gained another, but President Eisenhower spends practically all the Air Force money on B-52s for the Strategic Air Command. Bob wears nothing more on his sleeve but has lots of time in grade.

He does, however, have only about eight months more to put in before his discharge, because he applies for and gets approved for an early out to go to college. His actual discharge date is October 10, but in late August he is a civilian for the first time in three years, nine months and twenty-seven days. On the last day he takes a discharge physical and an audiometer reveals tone deafness, probably from sleeping so close to the flight line at Osan, where two Sabre jets on the PSP scrambled every three minutes, twenty-four hours a day.

Stay another day, the technician tells him, and he'll qualify for a disability pension.

Nothing will keep him another day.

Chapter Twenty-four
The Will and the Way

College occupies his mind of course. He has long wanted it and his officer in charge at Dobbins told him he needed it. Months ago he devised a plan to get there. It includes a low-cost college with daytime classes, a morning newspaper that will hire him to work nights, and nearby housing. The triple target: Castleton State College (one day to be Castleton University), the *Rutland Herald* and his mother's house on Main Street in Rutland, only twelve miles east of the college town. Three proposal letters earn positive responses. He becomes a full-time student and a full-time reporter simultaneously, with a room for precious little rest.

Morning paper working hours of 2 p.m.-11 p.m. or 6:30 p.m. to 3 a.m. fit him perfectly but the loud ring of the alarm rouses him rudely for classes that begin at 8 a.m.

He snubbed Castleton five years ago when accepted by Marquette, Syracuse and Seton Hall, schools he could not afford to attend. But now it looks great—no more a stock clerk, he is a bona fide college boy. If being an enlisted man saluting an officer taught him anything it's the value of a degree. He has felt five years behind his high school classmates. But one of his fellow reporters has just been graduated from college and this is his first real job. He's the same age as Bob, who suddenly realizes he has caught up. Sure, he must study at the same time, but no longer does he feel outpaced in the marathon of life.

Because of his military experience as a writer and editor, maybe even a bit ahead.

In the classroom as a twenty-three-year-old freshman among classmates five years younger, he's miles ahead. An English major, he remembers reading in the barracks much of what's new to the teenagers. When it comes to producing essays and term papers, his writing and typing skills provide a distinct advantage. Practically no freshmen know how to type, having been college preppies not admitted to typing courses, as was Bob, save the influence of Sister Imelda. Nor have they been required to type on the job for five years. His neatly typed papers probably earn him one grade higher than they otherwise might just because the prof doesn't need to struggle through the hen scratching of all the other students. He thinks typing is the best thing he ever learned in high school. And writing ability helps him embellish prose for the profs with hyperbole when facts lay beyond recall.

He leads a double life. Mornings he's a college boy. Afternoons and evenings, sometimes late into the night and early the next morning, he's a newsman. Sleep? Not much. Study? Some, in the wee hours. Because he knows head writing, layout, type specification and photography and film processing, he finds himself filling every position in the newsroom, including those on the late shift. Most of the work concludes at the first edition deadline of eleven, but when he fills in for the sports or night editors, often drunk or hung over, he stays until one, even though there's seldom much to do. He does update the sports page with west coast baseball scores and there is often the late auto accident or air catastrophe that require new leads on wire copy.

That means sending new copy to the composing room, where sometimes it's keyed into a Linotype machine by Ben Hurley, George's father. Ben works until 3 a.m., a schedule he's had for years, and one that's kept him asleep during most of daylight hours. He had little interaction with his son, who got no attention from his father to speak of during most of his childhood. George has received much attention since—from law enforcement. He robbed a bank and went to the state prison. Let out early to join the army during the Korean War, he soon earned a cell in the stockade, then broke out, stole an army truck and nearly ran over a military policeman signaling him to stop at the main gate. That brought him twenty-five years in Leavenworth Prison.

Small-town newspapering produces a few big moments. Bob spends two days trying to find and photograph Liz Taylor and Richard Burton, honeymooning on Mendon Mountain. Bob's mother, cooking in a restaurant on the mountain, tips him off that they are staying in a motel there. Bob knows the owner, Henry Veghte, but, sworn to secrecy, he denies their presence. Bob fails to find them.

With the coming opening of the New York World's Fair he attends a press preview there and meets Walt Disney. In his photographer role he and sportswriter Dave Hakins also drive to the city for the first game at the new Shea Stadium and he's happy to see Don Drysdale of the Dodgers beat the Mets.

One night a drunken George Fitzsimmons arrives at the newsroom door, waving a shotgun, saying he's looking for his cousin, who works downstairs in the pressroom. George says he wants to shoot up the place. Bob grabs a telephone and pulls it down with him under the keyhole desk. He calls the cops and Patrolman

Ralph Muscatello, a former football player, tackles George to end the threat.

A different kind of threat occurs when he inadvertently swaps a picture of the new Proctor school superintendent with that of a convicted rapist, complete with the wrong caption. He placates the superintendent with a corrected photo, an apology, and a season press pass to the racetrack at Saratoga Springs, something he received because of his stints on the sports desk.

One afternoon a caller reaches Bob with a request to keep his name out of the paper. Charged with DWI, he says reading about it will kill his mother because of her heart condition. Bob tells him it's his job to put news in the paper, not keep it out and that the caller's job is to make sure his mother does not read the paper.

Bob interviews Probate judge George Jones, who prevented adoption of a black child by white foster parents. He refused to sign a birth certificate showing a black child born of white parents, a genetic impossibility. That keeps her out of first grade, because a birth certificate is mandatory for entry. Bob's story goes all over the country via the Associated Press. He gets some colorful quotes, no pun intended, from the judge.

"Well, she's not exactly as black as the ace of spades, but she's definitely chocolate milk color," the judge tells him in his chambers. The two of them are there alone so Bob produces no pencil and notepad, a technique he uses to get good quotes when no third party can testify to the truth or accuracy. Interviewees relax and open up in that situation and nobody can deny their statements in case he doesn't get their responses word for word. That includes the judge, who calls him the next day.

"I had no idea you would print that. I'm not saying I didn't say it but I can't believe you would put it in the paper."

"Judge, you have been dealing with reporters for years and you know anything you tell them might wind up in print."

The story gets a big play in southern papers. It also gives a young lawyer, Phil Hoff, the opportunity to take the case to the state supreme court. Bob's story and ensuing publicity propel him to the governorship—the first Democrat in a hundred years to gain that Vermont office. Politics will never be the same in Vermont. The judge, re-elected for thirty years, gets turned out of office the next election day.

When JFK dies from an assassin's bullet Bob puts out an extra edition, the first one the paper has had since VJ Day. The managing editor is out of town, so Bob takes it upon himself to organize the staff and to write headlines for the AP stories and lay out the front page.

Simultaneously though, night editing gives him time to hit the books. And then he waits until the paper comes out to see if everything turns out as hoped. If that isn't late enough, he might then repair to somebody's house with the reporters, probably old John Clement's mansion, and drink beer for a couple of hours. It's no wonder he even sometimes falls asleep in a classroom. Once, about midnight, he actually falls off a chair in the newsroom.

The fact is, however, he's getting through college and winning promotions, primarily because he can do everything in the newsroom and is willing to do it. He's the Thursday sports editor, the Friday city editor, the Sunday managing editor and most anytime the night editor because the guy whose job it is often fails to appear, mostly, in the famous traditions of newsmen, because he is either drunk or hung over.

Part Two: After

Chapter Twenty-five

Biggest Challenge, Best Change

The Breck Girl emerges from another era, visible through a *Herald* window. She works on the second floor of the insurance company next door. The newsroom, above the pressroom, equals the elevation of that second floor and they can see each other through their office windows.

She quickly looks away when he spots her watching.

At age twenty-four he wants to buy a car. Mandatory insurance for a single male under twenty-five costs more than the car he can afford. He chides her about it during a chance meeting on the sidewalk out front, but of course she doesn't make the rules. She writes him a policy as if he is a year older. She says she doesn't care if found out because she'll marry soon and move to New York State. Bob buys a '58 Triumph and drives himself to school.

Miss Charming agrees to date him on off-duty Saturday nights. They have other chances to get together off campus because he bargains, with a four-hour pay minimum, to be on-call at the newspaper for any newsworthy events that might occur when everybody else is off, primarily on Saturdays because no Sunday edition is published. So, with a winter carnival at Middlebury College, he takes the camera, the company car and Miss Charming to a concert and a hockey game, plus dinner, all on an expense account.

While she makes good money, he's afraid of marriage, knowing full well that if a baby appears he will be the sole breadwinner, and that will mean poverty. But he's more afraid of letting her slip away.

On a Saturday afternoon he will photograph a high school football game in West Rutland. He picks her up in the newsroom car on the way at her home in Center Rutland. He parks and reaches into the camera bag but instead of a 200-millimeter telephoto lens he pulls out a $275 pear-shaped diamond engagement ring. She talks about a wedding the following June. He stalls her for six months though, until the following December, with school out for Christmas vacation, and that's when they are wed.

He loses his nerve at the door of St. Peter's Church, where he had been baptized just fifteen years earlier, so his mother slips him a tranquilizer. It's a nuptial Mass of course and lasts forever, but the pill keeps him mellow. She's absolutely lovely and cool of course but he sweats through the whole thing. When the Mass finally concludes and the deed is done, they ride to a photo studio for very nice formal photos, and then to the reception at the Nineteenth Green Restaurant in Center Rutland.

When the tranquilizer wears off at the reception he's nervous again. He gulps the wine set before him, and then grabs hers plus that of his best-man brother, both ushers and the maid of honor. The mashed potatoes that come with the chicken dinner clog his mouth like cotton batten. He drinks some more wine. His hands won't stop shaking. He forces a smile while fellow newsman Ken Wild flashes photos for their album but finally can't stand it any longer. Right after the requisite cake cutting and bouquet launching he leans over and whispers in her ear, "Let's get out of here."

The band plays, they step to the dance the floor and he steers her toward the rear of the room. Then, without saying goodbye to anyone they waltz out the back door and hop in the Triumph. They stop at their apartment where she dons a matching green suit and coat topped by a marabou hat. He changes from his monkey suit morning coat to a jacket and tie. Now he's calm and comfortable and drives forty-five miles to the Queensbury Hotel in Glens Falls. They dine in the hotel that evening and after breakfast there he steers the Triumph down the Northway and Thruway to New York.

Navigating down the Eastside Highway, which is what he still calls it even though for years it's been the FDR Drive, he exits too early and nervously finds himself on First Avenue in Spanish Harlem. But he guns it down Second Avenue. Luckily, the lights remain green just about all the way until an easy right on 41st Street and then east and another right to the Lexington Hotel.

It's New Year's Eve, but the drive, which features stretches of ice and snow, wears them out. So after dinner in the hotel Hawaiian Room, enjoying its national radio floor show, they celebrate the arrival of the New Year by looking out the window of their room and watching drunks on the street below.

The now calm and confident bridegroom, a native New Yorker after all, will be the first to show her the town. In the morning, bundled against the January cold, they step out to the street. She wants to see the Christmas windows on Fifth but first he shows her the lions at the library.

Department stores excite her. She pauses at Bergdorf-Goodman and B. Altman, but then gets excited at Lord & Taylor, Arnold Constable and oh, Saks Fifth Avenue. She hates to keep moving, but it's too cold for her to study the stores. So it's up the avenue and past Tiffany's and on to Central Park and it's zoo. The newly opened

Guggenheim features Jackson Pollack drips and drops of spattered paint of so-called art. The Metropolitan Museum of Art clearly appears more artistic to the couple. On the way back down the avenue they warm up at Radio City Music Hall for the Christmas show with the Rockettes, followed by a Rockefeller Center lunch and a look at the skaters. They duck into St. Patrick's Cathedral across the street. Then it's over to Times Square for supper at Toffenetti's, the one-thousand seat restaurant known as the biggest eatery on the busiest street in the world.

The next day the Stage Deli massive pastrami on rye does not move her, nor does Bob's choice, Saito's, run by the same restaurant in Tokyo. Jazz and steak at a basement dive in the Village don't excite her anywhere as much as the Fifth Ave shops, which they revisit the next day. Then they see the Broadway play "Sound of Music," which they both enjoy. It never occurs to Bob to take her to the Statue of Liberty, the Empire State Building or the U.N. because, after all, he's a New Yorker and they never go there. He'd like to go to the Garden for hockey but figures she wouldn't. In truth, he's torn between hitting all the cliche' spots she'd expect and introducing her to something different.

What she really would like to do is trim the trip and head for their new home on Butterfly Avenue in Rutland, so after just three days they check out of the Lexington and aim the Triumph to the north.

Chapter Twenty-six
The Apartment

With her money, she furnishes their apartment, one with a monthly rent of seventy-five dollars, twenty-five shy of his weekly salary. Four equal size, comfortable rooms constitute the second floor of the Dutch colonial on the southeast side of town, with a private front entrance, and a jolly Italian widow landlady downstairs who makes pizza and will send some up. When her husband Louis died, she converted the second floor, putting in a kitchen, and what became a living room, a den and a bedroom. They fill the four corners, with a full bath off the center hall. Electricity, heat and hot water come with the cost.

The newlyweds control the comfort level because they have their own thermostat, with the heat included in the rent. Their private entrance is the front door to the downstairs and upstairs halls. It is flanked by locked French doors. The missus and her mother found the place in a nice neighborhood with well-kept homes and yards.

The first morning Mrs. Charming and Dependable makes breakfast. She places a cup of coffee on the table before him. While he has tasted the brew with caffeine before, he hardly ever drank a cup, not even all that time in the Air Force, where a coffee pot never seemed to be more than six feet away.

"You're a married man now," she tells him. "You're allowed to drink coffee."

He learns he's not allowed to smoke cigarettes in the apartment.

"You are not going to stink up the curtains, or the furniture," the stickler for style and sanitation tells him.

In fact, he learns it's not okay to smoke them anywhere.

So he quits, but in a weird sort of way. He started smoking them in high school, when some kids considered it cool. A pack of Camels cost seventeen cents. When he went into the Air Force, the base exchange sold them for thirteen cents. He should have quit during basic training, when the drill instructor forbade recruits to smoke for the first two weeks. Then one day, the DI, supposedly granting t a great favor, demanded, "If you've got 'em, smoke 'em."

That one command he could finally disobey, so he didn't fire up a Camel. But he kept puffing when boot camp concluded. Overseas, the cost of Camels was only eleven cents. Upon discharge, the civilian smoker paid a quarter a pack and considered quitting because of the cost. But he was a newsman now, and smoking cigarettes, hey, that's what they do. Practically everybody in the newsroom smokes cigarettes, they are newshounds after all, and certainly have seen all the movie newsrooms where reporters seem required to slouch at typewriters with ties loosened, fedoras pushed back and cancer sticks on their lips. Nobody minds that smoke or smell.

Ken Wild, the exception, reeks the room with the smoke of cheap cigars. It hovers in clouds and catches a lot of criticism. In self-defense, Ken offers free samples from boxes of stogies on his desk, seeking accessories to the crime of stench, hoping to prevent assault on his habit.

Bob tries one. It's big and black and strong. He inhales once to learn that's not only unnecessary but unwise. He's dizzy. He soon knows to puff slowly and now can enjoy them without inhaling.

And without missing the cigarettes.

It's 1961 and the U.S. Surgeon General reports that smoking cigarettes can kill. Bob says lots of smokers ought to cease but knows there's no easy way. Cigars, he says, are the answer. You can hold them and puff on them without habit-forming inhaling. That fact puts in print a thrice-weekly column.

Pseudonymously he calls it "Quit Along With Clyde" and as Clyde Barnstable he quits cigarettes by substituting cigars. He chronicles Clyde's progress for a couple of columns and the next thing he knows cases of cigars arrive at the office. Based on a spike in sales attributed to the column, local distributor Quebec Cigar Company contributes enough stogies to supply the entire newsroom for months.

Meanwhile, *Mrs.* Charming and Dependable, makes it clear she controls the household. She had selected the maple Early American style living room furniture and announces that she alone will dictate the decor. He's okay with that and it's a good thing, because there are no two ways about it. He will learn though, in years to come, maple will give way to cherry, mahogany and walnut. Potential comfort in any chair will bow to style. Queen Anne reproductions will replace what's here now.

Sometime, if she can swing it, she will acquire all the furniture in Queen Anne's castle.

A junior now, he just begins to see the light at the end of the college tunnel. He drives the two of them in the Triumph to the college in the mornings. He leaves for the office about one and she rides home with a co-worker when her day is done at five. About six she serves supper.

The youngest of eight, including three sisters, she is only learning to cook. He arrives home one night to find her crying in the kitchen, failing to roll out piecrust dough because it clings to the pin. As his mother had taught him, Bob pulls a handful of flour from the cannister on the counter, with a flourish sprinkles the pin and in a flash rolls the dough flat.

The dumbest thing he's ever done in a kitchen results in barring him from cooking there for half a century. From that night on there will be no role in the kitchen for him. One does not show up Mrs. Charming and Dependable like that.

In the classroom, Dr. Tilley, the new chairman of the English Department, taps Bob to edit a booklet of classmates' essays. That's the good news. In the botany lab, there's both good and bad. First, the good, he gets a lab bench partner who was a boyhood local baseball idol. Ten years earlier Bob cheered a seventeen-year-old centerfielder for the Rutland Royals, a Class D minor league baseball team in the now-defunct Northern League. Elder (Hap) Haapala, a fleet blond from Flushing, hit for high average and ran down long drives.

Now he finds Hap beside him on the bench.

"What are you doing here?" Bob asks. "I thought you were playing ball."

Hap explains that he signed with the Yankees and played for Albany, the Double A farm team there. Yes, he hit 'em and caught 'em and went hopefully to spring training with the big club for three years. Another blond centerfielder, this one from Oklahoma, went there too and blocked him.

"He plays for the Yankees now. You know him. He hits the ball harder than I did. So I decided to marry a Rutland girl and go to college to be a phys ed teacher. That's why I'm here.

"I'm no Mickey Mantle."

The bad news: Hap, on the bench, helps very little with botany, in fact needs some. Failing the course but needing the credit to graduate, Bob takes time off from the paper and pulls an all-nighter. Only his top score on the final exam earns him the three credits he needs.

Top scores don't aways mean much. The history prof claims she grades on a curve. Bob turns in the top exam but gets only a *B*. He asks her how come. She replies that the exam is too difficult for anyone to get more than a *B*. Go figure.

With a minor in education, at graduation Bob applies for a Vermont teaching certificate, because a classroom job could back up a journalism career. The chairman of the state board of education writes him, denying his application, saying he's short nine credits in physical education. The state colleges board earlier ruled that serving four years in the military substituted for college phys ed classes and so the college properly conferred nine credits toward his eventual degree.

Go figure.

He shrugs it off, with no desire to teach, although years later two colleges will hire him as an adjunct instructor. Already earning more at the paper than first-year teachers, he's always preferred journalism anyway. He completes his degree requirement in three and a half years, having amassed the requisite hundred and twenty-eight credits by carrying as many as twenty-one per semester. He can't get out of there fast enough and impatiently waits until the end of May to join Sir Edward Elgar's Pomp and Circumstance march to a bachelor's degree.

He waits no longer for promotion to city editor. Even as a student he had acted in that capacity for several months because of the prolonged illness and, finally, demise of Ed Schriftgieser, the Harvard grad and classmate nemesis of the English prof who accused

Bob of plagiarism. But now publisher Bob Mitchell, who hired Bob after the Air Force, makes the position official, announcing it in the paper and delivering a fairly decent raise, plus a "key man" life insurance policy. At twenty-six, Bob becomes the youngest city editor since the birth of the *Herald* in 1794. It's timely because now with great excitement a new member of the Butterfly Avenue household arrives on a surprisingly warm and rainy pre-dawn day in January. Now the erstwhile den becomes a nursery for Robert Scott.

Mrs. Charming and Dependable, now promoted to full-time mother, quits her bursar post at the college, although the state college trustees contract with her for consulting, primarily for pre-audits at their three other institutions of higher learning. She trains her successor too, but he's no full replacement, for he requires an assistant and expensive new accounting equipment. Even with that he can't do what she did for years and is dumped for another, also tutored and further developed by Mrs. C&D.

It's a very good year so far. Not only does son Bob arrive, but the beloved Dodgers win the World Series in four straight. Bob witnesses the first game in person at Yankee Stadium, sitting in the center-field bleachers with brother-in-law Leo Bartlett. They had no tickets when they got to the stadium so stood in line for a couple of hours before the afternoon game began. They paid $1.50 for the seats and were lucky to get them. They watched Sandy Koufax strike out 15.

So far so good for Bob, but not for the subject of the first *Rutland Herald* extra edition ever published. Fifty years later, Rob Mitchell, grandson of the publisher, will write an account of that edition, which appeared the afternoon of November 22, 1963.

The Nov. 22, 1963, extra edition announced President John F. Kennedy's assassination. That November day was one that is burned into the memory of the people who lived through it.

The extra edition came together quickly in the hours after the news sent the nation into mourning.

The newspaper's managing editor was not on duty that day. Kendall Wild was in North Carolina with reporter Tony Marro, looking into the status of a Rutland Baptist minister who had been arrested in connection with his "action for civil rights."

It was Bob Bennett, then filling the role of city editor, who more or less made the decision to publish an additional edition. Bennett, now 77, can't remember if he was the one to make the final call. He just knew the newspaper had to do something.'

"I wasn't due to go in," he said, as Friday was his day off. He heard the news of the murder in the early afternoon. "I said I'd better get down to the paper because we've got to do something."

He heard the news of the murder in the early afternoon. Bennett had graduated from Castleton State College that June after four years in the service and four years working for the Herald while taking classes. He got in around 1 or 2 p.m. and found the newsroom mostly empty. In those days the print deadline was 3 a.m. so reporters came in to work around 2 p.m., and editors around 6:30 p.m.

He started ripping wire copy off the teletype machines and writing headlines. When he had a headline done he'd put it in a canister that went into a pneumatic tube and off to the composing room where it was set in type. 'Frantic Efforts to Save Stricken President, 46, Fail in Dallas Hospital' read one. 'Police Nab Man With Gun' read another.

Bennett thought hard about the lead headline and settled on 'Assassin Kills President; Kennedy Shot in Car'. The first two pages of the Extra were built in a few hours. By 6 p.m. the presses were running to print the 8,800 copies of the four-page edition.

"'We thought we were really doing something significant," Bennett said.

While Bob's salary now meets all the bills, he worries about the future if still another member joins the family, so he decides to shoot weddings on the side. Instead of full-time student while full-time newsman, he now toils a mere forty hours, five days a week most of the time, and weddings occur on Saturdays. He rigs up darkroom equipment in the bathroom and develops and prints black and white pictures.

Of all the work he has ever done, wedding photography is the worst. Every bride-to-be insists on every cliche' shot in her girl-friends' albums. That's the easy, if boring part. Catholic weddings aren't too bad, because a Nuptial Mass affords time for shots both at the altar and from the choir loft. Protestant services challenge him with brief ceremonies and ministers who frown on flashbulbs, requiring fast work with only the light available in dimly lit churches.

Church ceremonies follow time-honored, prescribed tradition but receptions can be unruly. Expected poses include cutting the cake, bouquet tossing, the first dance, etc., and he must politely but firmly orchestrate their sequence because the principals seldom know what's next. The days of wedding planners to conduct this merry band lies far in the future. Exuberance and drunkenness of those in attendance further complicate all cooperation with the photographer.

Bob shoots every shot on two cameras. Holding his breath, he develops the film rolls separately in short sections; there is no returning for a retake. When the bride comes back from Bermuda or wherever, he had better have every shot she had envisioned. Unquestionably, this is pressure.

Fortunately, it adds about a hundred a week to his newspaper salary, which just about makes up for the money lost when the bride becomes a stay-at-home mom.

Now that he's a college grad however, Bob envisions a salary far better than he could expect in a career at the *Herald*. Ken Wild, now the managing editor, occupies the next step on the ladder, a rung that Bob can never hope to reach. Ken succeeded the overweight and hard-drinking Bill Dexter, who suffered a fatal heart attack while cutting up a tree that fell in his yard. Bachelor Ken, whose dad edits the editorial page, is going nowhere and the owner-publisher serves also as editor in chief.

Bob discusses his future with his father-in-law, a man content to stay in the same capacity for the same company for fifty years. He can't believe Bob would abandon a position he considers as one of prestige. But the son-in-law wants to see what he can get elsewhere. Besides, he soon will need to be elsewhere because another baby is on the way. There is little room for him without sharing the den, later nursery, now bedroom, with a big brother.

Bob needs a mortgage.

Chapter Twenty-seven
Job Hunting

Bob and the bride check real estate, new and old in Rutland and environs. They like nothing they can afford. Bob recalls that best-paid Bill Dexter owned the only home on the news staff, with a mortgage simply because his wife taught school. Bob decides that at twenty-seven, with his experience and most of all a degree, he can earn a lot more if he leaves the small town.

On a bigger newspaper he'll have to join the guild, but even union wages won't win a mortgage. A rim man on the *New York Daily News* makes too little to buy a house in suburban New Jersey. An offer comes from General Electric after Bob visits a plant in Pittsfield, Massachusetts. The company needs an editor for its employee newspaper. It's a management position but the company employs union workers, and that turns him off once again, having covered contentious labor talks in town.

Eastman Kodak will hire him, certainly in part because of his plan to make every reporter also a cameraman, relying on the company's fast film, Tri-X. He interviews in Rochester, flying out of the Albany airport, for a job writing "How-To" books. While he's out there, he visits Xerox, thinking he might like to write for its internal house organ. On his way to Albany, his '62 Saab croaks in Glens Falls on the Northway, forcing him to hitch a ride the rest of the way, barely in time to catch his flight. He calls Rutland Saab dealer Russ Smith from the airport, who tows the car himself and sends a driver to meet his plane that evening and chauffeur him home from Albany. Smith says when you sell a weird car you need to provide wonderful service. Then, for free, he puts in a new engine.

Upon reflection, he figures Rochester lies too far afield and sustains more snow than Rutland, so he disqualifies both companies, disdaining their offers. Next, he drives to Corning and the Glass Works, for a publicity position.

Asked to return for a second interview with Mrs. C&D and toddler Robert Scott, two executives' wives take her to lunch and show her schools and real estate, really wanting to look her over, and when he gets home the phone rings with an offer. Unquestionably, his wife's presence and personality clinch the deal. Bob recalls that Vance Packard proclaimed in his book *The Pyramid Climbers,* that in Corning, an offer comes only if hypercritical company matrons say she passes muster.

Corning will be out of the question because his wife proclaims that "Corning is a dump," and that's a phrase their two-year-old singsongs every five miles all the seven hours to their home.

On the way they stop in Syracuse and stay overnight so Bob can discuss a similar position with Carrier Air Conditioning. When they leave the motel the next day they forget the kid's clothes and he rides home in pajamas. When Carrier calls with an offer, Bob begs for a couple of days to think about it, pending an interview at IBM headquarters in Armonk. He drives down there only to find that the position he applied for has been filled, that the manager who was to interview him went out of town but somebody else there wants to talk about a similar position on the company's *Think* magazine. Bob says no thanks and drives home, figuring he doesn't want to work for a company that can't even set up a proper interview.

Carrier phones while he is away, looking for a decision. Bob calls back and declines the offer, mostly because he doesn't want to go to Syracuse any more than Rochester. Receiving several offers, with comparable salaries, he considers himself a hot commodity. But if in Podunk and disliking the job he'll need to make another move. Forget it and face it: Bob moved nineteen times since he left New York as an infant.

He wants the next move to last awhile.

He needs a major league job, not one in the bushes. He craves a corporate headquarters, a home office with nowhere else to go. All the moves he made as a boy make him say he would never want that for his sons. He really wants to go to New York, where if you can make it there, the saying goes, you can make it anywhere. And if you can't do it at one place, you can walk across the street and win another job. That's security. In truth, he'd really love to live in the Jersey burbs, partly to relive his early childhood and partly so his children can.

So he sets his sights on the big city.

He revises his resume', and based on recent job hunting, adds the line "Married to a Corning Wife." When Bob replies to an ad in the New York Times, that gets the attention of Dick Allen, an employee relations exec at Chas. Pfizer & Co., in New York, which needs an assistant editor for its employee publications, a magazine, a newspaper and a bulletin. On the phone, Dick tells Bob that as a personnel guy, *The Pyramid Climbers* is a must read, and he clearly recalls the paragraph on Corning.

So in early August, Bob steers the Saab with its new engine to the city. Once again it's down the Northway and Thruway, to Jersey

Routes 17 and 46 and 3. Emerging from the Lincoln Tunnel, he takes it to the roof of the Port of Authority bus terminal, a cheap place to park and one that eliminates driving in city traffic. He walks across 41st and cuts through Bryant Park to Fifth Avenue at 42nd, careful not to peer at the tall buildings, the mark of a rube, and keeping near the curb. When he stops for the light he makes sure to look at the lions at the library. At the corner of Second Avenue, he pushes his way through the revolving doors of Pfizer World Headquarters and approves when he admires Vermont marble and granite gracing the lobby.

He rides the elevator to the sixteenth floor and reports to the receptionist, a smoky Haitian girl he will learn to hold in high regard. She ushers him into Dick Allen's office. The tall, crewcut interviewer seems like an easy-going guy. He wants Bob, who decides he wants Pfizer and they get right down to salary. Bob stupidly asks for $8,500, a thousand more than he's been offered lately, which is $2,500 more than the *Herald* pays.

Dick says he can't pay that.

Instead, he offers Bob $9,800, saying if he wants a starter home in a nice town in Jersey he will need at least that much. Then he says Pfizer will cover the move and complete maternity costs for second child, already on the way. Overwhelmed and impressed with the benefits and everything he sees and learns about Pfizer, he shakes on it and meets his new boss, Dick Shahan, manager and editor of employee communications, and two more future co-workers. Working for a company that makes a lot of the medicine that saves lives sounds good. If you are going to "go over the side," as his coworkers are certain to characterize it whenever anyone leaves journalism for the corporate world, how can it be better.

He agrees to start the Tuesday after Labor Day.

A two-week notice terminates his six years in the newsroom. That's no problem at the paper, where people come and go with regularity. He's been performing as the promotions editor, producing the special sections he introduced years earlier. "Fall Fashions" is almost ready and he has already selected and coached reporter Harry Levins for the city editor spot. It's not easy to leave your first real job—and the company that gave you your first chance after the service, one that let you make your way through college.

But when it's time to move on you do what you have to do.

If you are the man of the family.

Chapter Twenty-eight
The Metropolitan Area

If departing the *Herald* jolts Bob, moving to Jersey devastates his bride. Never living anywhere else than Center Rutland, she's surely devoted to her nearby parents. Brothers and sisters and childhood friends live here.

A visit to Gram Jones's home in Lafayette four years earlier on her hundred and fifth birthday showed Mrs. C&D that this part of Jersey, although lacking mountains, looks more like Vermont than Vermont does, complete with dairy cows and dirt roads. That's little help—Vermont is right here, New Jersey lies three hundred miles down the road.

But the next thing he knows she is researching all the towns within reasonable distance to the city. She wants a fashionable address with great schools and a wonderful hospital, because she will be going there soon to welcome son number two. It all adds up to Bergen County for its commuting convenience, the Village of Ridgewood for the Valley Hospital, and the adjacent Township of Wyckoff for their new home. She hopes to claim a two-story colonial, reminiscent of her childhood residence in Center Rutland. And it needs a fireplace, screened porch and a garage.

With two thousand dollars in the bank, they think they have enough for a down payment. Down the highways they go, directly to a real estate office in the middle of Wyckoff. Son Bob, now pushing two and a half, sleeps most of the miles away in the back seat of the Saab. When they pull into the parking area, the toddler declares the office is New Jersey, concluding it must be because that's where the car is going.

After seeing several colonials, reality settles in. They cost twice what they can afford. Instead, they put down $2,300 and buy a cape on Colona Street. It has four bedrooms, two up and two down, but no fireplace, screened porch or garage, not even a basement. It has in fact only what $23,500 can buy with a Federal Housing Administration mortgage.

It includes a handy storage shed attached to the back and a nice, if small, yard behind, the best part of the quarter-acre lot. A swing and a sandbox, two necessities, find plenty of space. And because it's on a tree-lined street in swanky Wyckoff, it has *location*.

Occupancy won't occur until late September but Bob must report early in the month to 235 East 42nd. The bride starts packing and her husband checks into the cheap and seedy YMCA hotel in the city. He would like to go home on the first weekend but that Saturday is the date of the annual Pfizer Family Outing, which takes place at the World's Fair in Flushing, now in its second year. Because the employee communications department is part of personnel, or, as they now call it, employee relations, he is assigned to the Outing, taking tickets. Of course he's been to the fair twice before, earlier in the year, first for the media preview and later at Vermont Day, when he rode there on a Vermont Transit bus with Rutland chamber of commerce people and of course Mrs. C&D.

Fifteen thousand metropolitan area Pfizer employees and their families enjoy the run of the fair. It's all theirs. Golden tickets admit them to every attraction on the grounds, plus lunch and participation in a raffle for color television sets. In prior years they converged at Steeplechase Park on Coney Island but that closed last year.

So he's stuck in the city on what's left of his *Herald* salary because Pfizer pays once a month and that's weeks away. Some of that goes for the final rent payment at Butterfly Avenue. Breakfast becomes the best deal of the day at basement counters along 34th street, not far from the Y. Lunch in the company cafeteria is another good deal but some days he just walks around the corner and gets a fifty-cent Sabrett hot dog, yummy when steamed in mysteriously brown water to emerge with a slathering of onions, sauerkraut and bright yellow mustard. For supper he sometimes tries the cheapest joint on Times Square, Tad's Steaks—only $1.99 for flame-broiled shoe leather.

As far as the Y room goes, nothing could be cheaper or creepier except a jail cell. Amenities include merely a radio, so he listens to Yankee and Met games. One night he decides to watch a game at Yankee Stadium and grabs a cab.

"I ain't goin' to the country tonight," the cabbie tells him when he says he's headed for the Bronx, which of course is part of the city. So he subways uptown to the stadium. When he returns to the Y, he learns somebody stabbed somebody to death in the lobby.

Meanwhile the Saab sits on top of the Port of Authority bus terminal, the cheapest place to leave it. In Rutland the bride drives her dad's red and white Oldsmobile.

Finally he moves the family to Wyckoff and meets some neighbors left and right and across the street, including two boys for son Bobby to play with. The bride likes the supermarket in the small shopping center and of course finds the shops in Ridgewood and the big stores on the highway, including Lord &Taylor and B. Altman's. Rutland has no shopping like this. Rutland? Where is that?

Mrs. C&D reveals her true colors as a retail aficionado. There's no stopping her shopping now. The Garden State Plaza and the Fashion Center—that's where it's at!

She's building a reputation Bob will say that if shopping becomes an Olympic event she will win all the gold medals—one each for specialty stores, strip malls, boutiques, department stores and shopping centers. Oh yes, furniture emporiums. She now has a house to fill.

Bobby gets a big bedroom on the second floor when John arrives in March to command a compact downstairs room that becomes a nursery. Another upstairs bedroom serves as a family room, with a studio couch and a television, divided by a bookcase Bob built, with a desk and his typewriter behind.

Inside, the bride says everything must be painted and papered to her taste. Meanwhile, outside the towering oak and beech trees in the backyard rain so many leaves that by Thanksgiving, when Bob finally rakes them up, they form a pile five feet high and fifty feet long.

Chapter Twenty-nine
Writing at Pfizer

Every weekday morning Bob walks three blocks to board the 7:15 bus to the city. Fellow commuters call the Short Line the longest distance between two points. In reality, if all goes well on the way along routes 17, 46 and 3 he will arrive in Secaucus at the Lincoln Tunnel to the Port of Authority bus terminal in fifty-five minutes. Then he'll walk past Times Square along 42nd to Second Avenue and be in his office on the 16th floor of Pfizer World Headquarters before 8:45.

Bob writes articles for the nationwide monthly magazine *Scene* and writes and edits most of *Pulse,* a weekly newsletter for the metropolitan area, along with an occasional news bulletin distributed to employees world-wide. Dick Shahan, who also lives in Wyckoff, manages the department and edits the magazine. Janet Merola, a plump twenty-something redhead, also writes for the publications. Stringbean Joanne Tagliaferro, just out of high school, serves as secretary for the department.

Bob has a lot to learn about Pfizer, with its rich history dating from 1849 when two German immigrants, Pfizer and Earhart, both named Charles, built a chemicals plant in Brooklyn. Now the world's largest producer of antibiotics, the company operates a huge research center in Connecticut and various facilities in much of the world. The company continues to expand exponentially. The president, John McKeen, busily makes acquisitions so he can meet his goal of "five by five" or half a billion in sales by the end of 1965.He spends a billion to get half that, so news of subsidiaries becomes plenty of stories.

When the company decides to dump the comic character Peter Pain, which helped sell Ben-Gay in Sunday newspapers for years, Bob writes his obituary, describing him as a "sonofawitch." Don Lum, VP of employee relations and Shahan's boss, changes it to "a witch's son."

One of the sales guys who lives in Wyckoff moves to the Midwest and back again. Bob chronicles his unusual real estate record, which includes building the same house from the same blueprints three times—the third back in Wyckoff. That story turns into extra income to Bob. He sells a version to the Sunday Magazine of the Bergen Record, the first of two stories he'd have published there.

Corporate writing isn't all fun, including explaining changes to employee benefits programs. The benefits manager, a lawyer, produces a legal document filled with a gallon of gobbledygook. Bob drains all that out of it and hears, "You can't put a quart in a pint jar." Bob replies that reducing his quart, a murky potion, will give readers a palatable swig. It's better, he says, to give readers a sip than let them die of thirst.

Shahan proves weak as a writer and editor, but strong as a planner and budgeter. He has a history of working for several companies and Bob thinks he has his eye on more. It won't be long before Dick proves him correct. A year later he leaves Pfizer for Sky Chefs, which supplies food service to airlines. Bob succeeds him as manager of employee communications and gets a good raise, which puts him up to $12,800. He now reports directly to Lum, also a member of the board of directors. The consummate executive type, Lum seldom makes a bad decision because he rarely makes any at all. His standard response to any suggestion: "I'll get back to you on that."

Don't hold your breath.

Needing a replacement, Bob recruits Dave Hakins, a *Rutland Herald* reporter and promising writer, someone he's known since Dave was a kid at Rutland High School, covering team sports.

Much source material for the magazine comes from the public relations department on the 22nd floor.

Tony Biesada and Joe Callahan there become mentors and friends. They often lunch together in deli-pubs up and down Second Avenue, as well as the restaurant downstairs, DeSantis, its name announced on a big window logo with a giant D and S. Bob's favorite lunch, rare ground beef with a thick slice of raw onion on rye toast, becomes popular with the patrons and makes the printed menu as a "Bob Burger."

Some afternoons Biesada transposes the letters on the window, telling his secretary he, Callahan and Bob will be at Scientific Design, a supposed commercial art studio, when instead they are downstairs sipping draft beer.

Janet Merola completes a master's degree in English at New York University, courtesy of the company, which pays seventy-five percent of the tuition. Bob aims for graduate school too. He thinks he'll earn an MBA, then learns that Fordham insists he take an undergraduate course in accounting before he can be admitted. That's not going to happen. Long ago he gave up on Columbia's journalism school because Ed Schriftgieser told him he already knew how to put film in a camera.

At NYU, he rejects the thought of an English major because he must read Beowulf for the third time, having suffered through it in high school and again at Castleton. If he learned anything from Beowulf it was never ever to read it again. He settles on the program American Civilization, figuring if he will be in public relations he will need to learn all he can about the American public. Concentrating on American literature lets him read authors he admires. Other subjects include history, journalism and political science. It's all very interesting but difficult. He must compete for grades with graduate students in each of those majors.

The company will pay three-quarters of the tuition but with a catch. Employees who are vets with the G.I. bill get nothing. Bob rewrites the company policy and suggests it to Lum, who agrees employees who served their country should get the seventy-five percent. So with the post-Korea G.I. Bill and Pfizer's contribution, Bob's tuition, books, carfare and dinner with a martini before class (two if he has to make an oral statement) cost him nothing. With at least five bucks left at the end of the month, he gets a master's at a profit. It takes him three years of Wednesday nights. That includes one extra semester when he takes a course toward a Ph.D. Figuring he's spending too much time studying, he quits after that to be Bobby's Little League coach.

The last year he writes his thesis on an author he considers transitional from the 19th to the 20th centuries, Stephen Crane. He's tired of Henry James, who describes every twig on every branch on every tree in the whole forest. Crane succinctly and picturesquely says an hombre is "dressed like a Mexican" (sans details of a sombrero or serape) and paves the way for the period of Hemingway. During his thesis seminar the prof who heads the American Civ program proclaims, "Liberal thought is clearly superior to conservative thought, and the proof of that is found in all the great books liberals have written, compared to but a few produced by conservatives."

Bob does not boost his possibility of thesis acceptance when he points out that conservatives *do* what liberals write about. It gains approval, however grudgingly, along with an imagined badge of courage, on the hundredth anniversary of the New Jersey author's death.

The degree happens to require another semester at Fairleigh Dickinson University in Hackensack for a French class. Twice he flunks the required Educational Testing Service exam of translating scholarly material from a foreign language into English. He last studied French in high school, sixteen years earlier. After a spring test failure he studies all summer. He takes it again in the fall and scores worse than the first time. Remember Dick Allen's smoky Haitian secretary? Now Josephine is Bob's. Her native language is French. She helps Bob get the grade he needs at Fairleigh Dickinson as a substitute for passing the language exam. Here's how: Bob devises a flattering letter to his plump and dowdy prof, in English. He tells her how much he has enjoyed studying under such a charming teacher, adding that if he should be so fortunate to obtain a *B* for the course that he desperately needs to get his master's, would she send it over to NYU at Washington Square. Josephine translates it. He copies her French in his own hand. When he slips it to the prof during the final she stops at his desk, reads it and smiles. Then she frowns.

"Robair," she says, "you did not write this."

"Ma Cher Madame professeur," he says, "it's not always what you know but who you know," and he tells her about Josephine. The prof makes him promise never to reveal her identity, then provides the *B* grade he requires. He sends her flowers. A few years later NYU decides the language exam is no longer needed, legitimizing, he thinks, his master's.

Writing for the Pfizer magazine requires traveling to company locations around the country. Sometimes he flies in a company plane but usually takes commercial flights to far-flung facilities. When he does he also shoots photos for the magazine, using his own Exakta single lens reflex equipment. Shahan didn't want him to shoot in the city, because he said Bob could put the photography budget in jeopardy. With Dick gone, Bob shoots everywhere and hires Modernage for processing, cutting the photo costs. Reducing department expenditures wins a raise.

After three years at Pfizer the new manager thinks his department ought to be under public relations, partly because so many stories originate there. Nothing doing says Lum. It used to be there and he moved it to his own bailiwick. So when his public relations pals, Biesada and Callahan, need another man and recruit Bob, he proposes he move there himself. Forget it, says Lum, he needs Bob right where he is. So if he can't go to the Pfizer public relations department he'll go to somebody else's. He finds a headhunter who specializes in supplying public relations types to big corporations that retain them. Security in this city, Bob reminds himself, is the ability to go across the street and get another job. Mobil Oil headquarters looms across 42nd street and west a block and that's where the headhunter sends him for an interview.

He wins a position in the public relations department as a writer for the company-wide newspaper, *Mobil World*. It appears in several editions for various divisions around the globe, including domestic refineries and oil fields ranging from Alaska to the Middle East. It's a huge department, with plenty of room for advancement. Oil always makes big news and only Exxon makes more of it.

He gives Lum a thirty-day notice, as called for in the employment contract.

The employee relations vice president fumes.

"You can't leave in thirty days! I can't possibly get another man-ager in that time."

Bob reminds Lum that he authored the employment contract himself, complete with that stipulation, but tells Don he'll ask Mobil if they will wait longer. Lum wants at least another month.

So the manager at Mobil says a month's okay and Bob agrees he'll stay, telling Don that because he will be getting two grand more per year, or $167 additional each month, he wants the difference. Says he owes it to his family.

Lum explodes. "You want to hold me up for more money? Hey, just go, and don't think you'll ever get another job at Pfizer."

Chapter Thirty
A Real P.R. Guy

Bob steps across the street. Dave Hakins and Janet Merola hold the fort at Pfizer until Lum hires Ellen Rochford as the new manager. Hakins doesn't like that and quits to go to Alaska as editor of an Anchorage newspaper. Later he joins J.C. Penney and First National City Bank, then Citibank, the latter a job that teaches him how to set up sports travel packages. Subsequently he starts his own sports travel company.

Bob's first morning at Mobil becomes a beaut, a real baptism of four-alarm fire. The media relations manager, Jack Gillespie, starts his vacation. The department head dispatches Bob to Jack's desk to field media questions with an appropriate response. As soon as he sits down all four of his phones figuratively burst into flames. Every newspaper in New York, plus the news magazines, wire services, radio and television stations want to know:

"What do you have to say now that Muammar Gaddafi has overthrown the monarchy in Libya and nationalized your oil fields?"

The first thing he does, with his hand over the receiver and under his breath, is to curse Gaddafi, not for stealing the company assets, but for giving him grief on his first day. He's supposed to draft a statement, run it by the department manager for review and approval, and respond. Bob doesn't even know Mobil is in Libya, let alone what should be said about it, but he writes a response and takes it to his new boss, Harold Olsen. He's downstairs in the Horn and Hardart Automat for coffee and pastry, a morning ritual. Bob shows it to Carol Nealon, the fetching redhead secretary, a former Miss Subways, whom he met only minutes before. She says he needs to run something this big upstairs to Rawleigh Warner Jr., the president and CEO.

Bob takes the elevator to the top floor of the silver skyscraper. Warner's secretary leads him into a lush office, paneled in mahogany over plush carpet.

He hands Warner what he wrote. The prez walks to a window and reads it. Then he trains a couple of eagle eyes on Bob.

"Who the hell are you?" Warner wants to know. "And where's Jack?"

This is all news to him. He phones his international division president, who knows nothing about it.

The calm, cool and collected chief executive is not.

He's furious.

"Look, I'll rewrite this myself and get it back to you."

Thankfully, Bob thinks, it's out of his hands. Olsen reappears in time to return the media calls. The rest of the week proves uneventful while the media plumb all the possibilities surrounding Mobil's loss to the new Mideast dictator.

Nevertheless, Bob decides to despise Gadhafi as long as the despot lives. Forty-two years later he rejoices, with no remorse, when rebels torture and murder him.

Mercifully more mundane than the task of facing the Libya crisis that first Monday is filling the pages of *Mobil World*. He interviews operations research specialists for a story about ideal gas station locations and oil deposits on the North Slope of Alaska and describes in the language of laymen how they do it. Just as he has long opposed jargon, that helps to hone an ability as a professional explainer. He needs it, no kidding, owing to his own naivety. He knows he's not the only one who dislikes the technological lingo and that it's his task to clarify it for everyone else.

He ghostwrites a photography series, for Mike Anguti, the company cameraman, with his own photos of his two sons. On assignment for Mobil Chemical, he gets a taste of proactive corporate publicity. He drives to the Finger Lakes region of New York, across Seneca from old Sampson air base, site of his first Air Force year. After a tour that includes hundred proof alcohol wine starter, he writes an internal piece plus a news release about a petroleum coke brick fire inversion to foil late season frost in the Taylor Wine vineyards. He also flies to the Lakeland area of Florida to produce news releases for the Tampa paper. They boast about benefits of land reclamation in the wake of phosphate strip mining.

After a year, a raise and promotion to editor of *Mobil World*, he wishes he could do more work with media, because that's where more money is. Then his phone rings. It's Tony Biesada, the Pfizer P.R. guy. The two have kept in touch. Often he joins Tony for lunch at one of the deli and beer dives on Second Avenue. Biesada makes an offer

"How would you like to come back to Pfizer? I need an assistant manager for two divisions, chemicals, and MPM, you know, minerals, pigments and metals."

"Sure I would, but it will never happen. Lum will never let me back in. He practically told me never to darken his door again."

"I'll take care of Don, just don't worry about that," Tony tells him.

A couple of days later he's sitting in Lum's office, just fourteen months since the last time.

"Welcome back!" he booms, extending his hand. "We're glad to have you. You can start with Tony as soon as you can leave Mobil. And I'm going to reinstate your time here toward a pension. Your record will show no gap in employment at Pfizer."

The world needs oil and he likes Mobil.

Pharmaceutical miracles keep people alive.

And Bob needs more money. Four thousand bucks more result because of his impression on Biesada.

It's a great surprise, but another soon presents itself.

Tony and Joe Callahan and Bob go to a dinner at the Princeton Club to hear a presentation by a P.R. practitioner at the New York Health Department. He's none other than Bob's last officer in charge, the erstwhile Captain Ray Porfilio, last seen seven years ago. Ray buys Bob a scotch before dinner and makes him an offer that Bob could only refuse.

"How would you like to join our Air Force reserve unit at the Wings Club in the Biltmore? We meet once a month. You don't get any pay, but you do get points toward a pension. Everybody in the unit is in some part of the media—news, advertising, publishing, television and radio—you name it. You can make a lot of connections and you'll never get called up for active duty because let's face it, we're all soft core.

"And everybody's an officer—but we could use an enlisted man. You could be him!" Bob's jaw drops.

"You need a flunky, don't you, somebody to take reservations and do other clerical or grunt work and salute a hundred other guys. Well, guess what? Now I have bachelor's and master's degrees, and back in Vermont I already turned down a direct commission in the reserve. You may recall that my father was a career army officer. He outranked you. I started in the military when I was six. I've had more than enough. I wouldn't stay one extra day back at Dobbins to get a disability pension.

"So I'm thinking you've gotta be kidding. To be the only enlisted man? How dumb do you think I am? I remember well you said I needed college. Well I got plenty. Thanks, but no damn thanks."

The Pfizer Building also houses the Manhattan offices of Bell and Howell, long a leader in film projectors and later cameras. In the lobby Bob runs into one of its public relations guys, Frank Bellamy, another guy from the Air Force, formerly a fellow staffer on the *Sabre Star* at Osan. He reported to Bob when he was editor. They go out to lunch and Bob tells him his company ought to come up with a hand-held scanner to replace the 3x5 cards used in research, especially, he says, for term papers, theses and dissertations in college. Frank likes the idea and says he will suggest it to the powers that be. A month later he reports that the brass thinks it would never sell, so forget it. Years later of course several companies produce such scanners, including Bell and Howell.

Student term paper researchers never had it so good.

Chapter Thirty-one
Where He Wants to Be

Up on the twenty-second floor Bob reaches his most recent goal. He promotes and defends the food-grade chemicals the company has created. Citric acid, found in all kinds of food and drink products, comes from a secret, unpatented concoction in the Brooklyn plant, which produces more of it than any other in the world.

The media, led by the *New York Times*, love to malign Pfizer preservatives as "poisons in your food." Regarding antibiotics, where Pfizer also leads the world, the media wring their typing fingers to foster the theory of transfer of resistance even though no case of it has ever occurred. As usual, most of the media continue to focus on spreading the ultimate persuasive motive of fear, resisting of course acknowledging iron-clad evidence of efficacy and safety.

For the Minerals, Pigments and Metals Division, whose products include several from limestone, clay and pyrolytic graphite, Bob visits several of its locations. One is on the Bushkill, a creek in Easton, Pennsylvania.

Pfizer extracts clay for its paint pigments from the same sources as the colors of Binney and Smith, the Crayola company, just upstream. Both companies certainly color the water and supposedly erode the city sewer system, requiring dealings with the *Easton Express*, the local paper.

Air pollution contributions emerge when the Easton plant marks its hundredth anniversary. Early glossy photos portray smokestacks actually enhanced by painting in clouds of fumes so they stand out against the sky. *Watch my smoke*, once a popular remark meaning productivity, succumbs to obliteration by airbrush, deleting, in the name of environmentalism, signs of pollution. Bob writes about the smokestack scrubbers recently installed.

Gibsonburg, Ohio, well might have been the inspiration for Sherwood Anderson's Winesburg, but right now Pfizer is turning the town white with layers of limestone dust. That calls for more publicity about how the Pfizer operation improves the standard of living there, plus the lawns and gardens.

Bob meets the mayor, also an employee, and the plant manager. They lunch in the town's only restaurant, which would have been a diner but for lack of a railroad car design. Bob picks up the lunch tab for three, including salad, porkchops, mashed potatoes and gravy, apple pie sliced in sixths, plus three Buckeye beers. It totals less than the bill for his hotel breakfast in Toledo. He files his expense report for the trip to an incredulous accounting department.

Duties as assistant manager for chemicals, minerals, pigments and metals soon give way to an opportunity in agriculture. The ag division needs a public relations manager and Bob wins the job. He becomes editor of *Agridynamics* magazine, mailed to 24,000 farm stores and 18,000 veterinarians. He also manages the Pfizer Research Conference, including hiring keynote speakers. Among them are the secretary of agriculture, Earl Butz; William Colby, the director of the CIA; Herman Kahn, the head of the Hudson Institute, "60 Minutes" newsman Morley Safer, astronauts from the moon mission Scott Carpenter and Michael Collins. Bob makes sure to get autographs for son Bobby, who has blossomed into a consummate collector.

The conferences take him all over the country, including Kansas City, where Bob spends a night in the presidential suite of the Muhlbach Hotel when no other rooms are available and he reminds the manager he controls the $50,000 budget spent there. The job includes plenty of contact with the ag press, whose members he hosts at hog farms in the Midwest and in Las Vegas for schmoosing and big show entertainment.

P.R. has its perks. The Pfizer box at Shea Stadium gives observation of the field from two rows behind the Mets dugout. The four seats and Diamond Club membership are supposed to be for visiting industrial customers, but the guys in the department keep them a secret. Bob takes his boys to see the Dodgers, including a couple of games when the fabled Sandy Koufax pitches. From their vantage point, his curve ball falls off the table. He also catches a foul popup from a pepper game off the bat of centerfielder Willie Davis. When son Bobby reaches over a gate to try to get an autograph, it opens and the five-year-old tumbles onto the field. A security cop nabs him by the collar and he starts to cry.

Manager Tommy Lasorda quickly tells him "Kwitcher cryin' kid," and hands him a baseball, turning tears into a smile.

Tom McGuire, the Pfizer security manager and a former FBI agent, asks Bob for two box seats, and says in exchange he will introduce him to Vin Scully, the Dodgers announcer. Seems he and Scully were roommates at Fordham. They go to the press box for a good chat, and that meeting leads to introductions by Scully to several Dodgers. Bob has a hamburger with Scully and Lasorda at their hotel in Atlanta, and the manager presents Bob to several of his players in the dining room. Even much later Bob will chat with Scully in Cincinnati and Montreal.

At Colona Street, the boys are growing bigger and gain a sibling. Late in July of 1970, just twenty-five hours after his own birthday, Bob finds himself at the Valley Hospital in Ridgewood, holding a tiny hand with fingers that look like they have just been manicured. They belong to Alyssa, the baby girl of the bride's dreams—a beauty destined to be a ballet dancer.

Her father is thrilled.

Alyssa completes the family of the man of the family.

Chapter Thirty-two

Rabbits and a Move

On one of the perpetual trips to Vermont to see the bride's parents, the children visit the Rutland Fair and the rabbit exhibit, where Bob showed his rabbits as a boy. They take home a pet Black Dutch they name Pickles, and weeks later, after a visit in Rutland to Tony Pisanelli, but of course, a buck they call Nickels.

Naturally, they produce a litter.

A neighborhood Boy Scout sees the backyard hutch and asks Bob to be his counselor for the Rabbit Raising merit badge. Bob reads the manual. It's woefully out of date—it's the same one Bob used twenty years earlier—so he writes the Boy Scouts with a proposal to produce a new one. They agree to pay him fifteen hundred dollars for it.

Publicity upon publication includes a *New York Times* article noticed at Garden Way Publishing, a Vermont company that produces books for country living, which results in an offer to write a complete book for adults as well as youngsters. The merit badge booklet is not the only publication out of date. The author of that one, George Templeton, ran the USDA rabbit experiment station east of Los Angeles and authored an ag school text, *Rabbit Production*.

Government and feed store publications recommended antiquated facilities and procedures, as did a few other old rabbit books. Rising real estate prices ran the rabbits out of the LA area to the Ozarks and President Eisenhower closed the station. Then Templeton died.

With a lined yellow pad on his commuter bus to New York, Bob writes one called *Raising Rabbits the Modern Way*, based on the updated information he provided in the merit badge book, along with wisdom he learned from Tony Pisanelli, and some tips in hutch construction he developed himself. He types it upstairs on his Royal standard on five Saturday mornings and sends it off to the editor, Walter Hard Jr., who accepts it and hands it off to another editor, Ed Miller. Miller recommends several changes which conflict with Bob's recommended practices. After some back and forth correspondence, Bob finally tells Miller there will be no capitulation, and if he doesn't want it the way Bob writes it he will send it somewhere else. Miller relents, publishes the book and soon leaves the company. Bob only wonders why.

Meanwhile he builds a battery of three hutches and installs them in the shed at the back of the house. He begins to breed pedigreed Dutch and put them in shows in the region. With success he begins to advertise Dutch and later Tan breeding stock in the rabbit magazines, shipping them all over the country from Newark Airport. Those individuals that don't measure up sell quickly in a pet store in town, which also sells wire hutches as fast as Bob builds them inside the shed.

With three children now, the inside of the house on Colona Street shrinks. Outside, Bob yearns for a bigger back yard because his plans for the rabbits are growing. The stylish and classy Mrs. C&D searches for houses around Wyckoff. She still covets a two-story colonial. The houses she likes cost $50,000 when they qualified for only half of that. Now a hundred grand, they remain out of reach, even though the couple sells Colona Street to Dave and Jane Hakins for more than twice the price five years earlier.

They certainly don't mind leaving the neighbors. On one side, the drunken Joe O'Donnell wants to borrow dough. Bob's pastor says don't lend him any because he will just use it to buy booze. In the back, effluent from a septic tank flows to their property. Across the street lives a somewhat spooky woman who never speaks to anyone. And on the other side, taking the prize, are the Smiths.

On a Friday, the bride drives their first new car, a Ford, up their driveway, its first trip from the dealership. The Smiths' overgrown woody shrub scratches the side of the sixty-seven sedan. That evening Bob walks next door to ask Smith to trim the bush because its branches droop over the driveway. The family's away for the weekend, so Bob trims it neatly. It had never scratched their skinny Saab.

Monday evening Bob walks up the driveway from the bus stop, to be greeted by a scowling George Smith.

"Did you trim my shrub?" he asks, really as more of a demand to know.

"Yeah," Bob replies, "it scratched our new car on Friday, the first day we got it. If you don't keep it trimmed I'm going to cut the goddamn thing down."

The two families never spoke again.

Mrs. C&D examines an expanded ranch in a nice neighborhood on Lawlins Road, accompanied by a local real estate agent. It's owned by a fellow Shortline commuter, who tells Bob a story about it on the bus. Transferred by Shell Oil to New York from Chicago, he bought it without his wife seeing it.

Now she has and hates it.

Cosmetically it's in bad shape inside and out. It surely needs paint everywhere and new roof shingles but the location, the bones of the place and the backyard are exceptional. With a finished playroom in the basement, a family room, fireplace, garage and screened porch—it includes everything they want. His bride wants to like it but, seldom a visionary, is leery because of its superficial looks.

Bob sees possibilities and says they can perk it up.

Clearly it's not in move-in condition; if so the place would cost way more than they can pay.

Nevertheless, the price is still too high. It's out of reach. Forget it.

Then Bob learns that Home Equity Corporation will sell it for Shell because it will transfer the guy on the bus to Louisiana. Home Equity wants $55,000 but Bob and Mrs. C&D offers $49,000, every cent they could hope to get from their bank. Bob phones Home Equity and says the couple will buy it "sight unseen," which technically is true. That means Home Equity won't have to pay, Bob points out, any real estate commission or advertising costs. The company says it will accept forty-nine-five and a ninety-day closing, with access to the key, plenty of time to paint, paper, carpet and scrape and sand doors and woodwork chewed and scratched by two English setters. After the dumbfounded real estate agent buys a full-page ad in the nearby *Ridgewood News*—for a house already sold-- he learns it was sold out from under him.

Bob and the bride slave away all summer. They paint, they paper, they replace baseboards. They reach into an oven and pull out a baked-in mitten. A pocket door won't close completely between the kitchen and dining room. It will give up a Wheaties box. Bob builds cabinets and bookshelves in the family room, even a walnut grandfather clock with a moving moon dial and Westminster, Whittington and Winchester chimes. Day after day they deliver some of their belongings to the new home.

He and Dave rent a U-Haul truck. In one morning they move the rest of their furniture out to Lawlins Road. In the afternoon they haul the Hakins household into Colona Street.

They split the hundred-dollar cost of the truck.

Chapter Thirty-three
How to Sell Books

Bob builds an eight by twenty-four-foot shed back in the trees, paints it dark green, installs thirty-six all-wire hutches and an automatic watering system. He partners with friend John Dack to raise Tans— he with Chocolates and Lilacs and John with Blacks and Blues. Bob shows John how to build a shed in his yard, just like one in his book. Bob continues to advertise and ship Tans from Newark Airport.

All excited with himself because he has finally authored a book after writing news, magazine articles and promotional material for years, he wants to see big sales. Garden Way robustly promotes the book by direct mail and to bookstores but results disappoint the new author.

Bob orders a dozen copies. He gets fifty percent off as an author. The next time he needs more rations for the rabbits, he takes the books to the feed store in Ramsey. He tells the owner the books will sell there because rabbit raisers come in regularly and will see the book repeatedly. Not only will he make some money, he won't waste time with customer questions. The answers are in the book.

"Look around," the merchant replies, "What do you see? Does this look like a bookstore? Forget it."

Unfazed, Bob says, "Just put a few on the counter. You can have them on consignment. If they move keep half. If they don't sell I'll take them back."

"Okay, because you're a good customer, but not on the counter. You can put them back there behind the gloves and pliers. I reserve the counter for impulse hot sellers."

Two weeks later Bob returns to Ramsey for more rabbit feed and gets a surprise that makes him smile and scratch his head.

Six copies sit on the counter.

"I see you have sold half of the dozen, but how come now the rest are on the counter?"

"I didn't just sell six—these are what's left of the second dozen. I ordered twelve more myself from the publisher. They gave me their bookstore discount, forty off."

Excited, Bob writes Jack Williamson, the Garden Way publisher, and tells him he ought to sell to feed stores because besides the rabbit book several other titles about livestock consume feed sold there. Jack's got books about chickens, sheep, cows, pigs and goats.

"They all eat what the feed stores sell. You'll sell more books in a week in a feed store than a bookstore will move in a year."

Jack writes back and says he has no sales force for feed stores, doesn't know how to reach them, doesn't know what discount they need and has no displays.

It's not going to happen.

Jack says what the store owner said at first. So one of the two knows it can happen. Jack will be the second.

Soon.

On Lawlins Road, Bob learns the street was named for the family just across the way. The current, sole occupant, Mrs. Lawlins, is a widow who teaches ballet in a basement studio. The youngest students are five, but Alyssa inserts herself into a class at age three, after accompanying her father to the broad and sunny Lawlins backyard. Some evenings Mrs. Lawlins sips martinis while slamming Ping Pong balls at Bob. Her late husband was an avid vegetable gardener. She says he can till the soil there if he splits the harvest with her. At the same time, Mrs. C&D becomes a Gray Lady at Valley Hospital and a volunteer at the school library. The boys play baseball and their dad coaches Bobby's team to the town championship

The family attends St. Elizabeth's Church, where the pastor announces, in the wake of Vatican II, that henceforth all hymns will be sung in the vernacular. The first one is *Kumbaya* and Bob wonders whose vernacular that could be. He imagines Sister Jane Frances, she of the chancel choir and Gregorian Chant, flipping in her grave.

On the job in the Pfizer ag division he wins a promotion to marketing services director. Public relations, advertising, sales promotion, marketing research and technical writing now report to him and he gets another raise. He writes speeches for Rollie Hendrickson, president of the division, and represents the company to trade associations such as the Pork Producers and National Broiler Council on matters of publicity and advertising. He becomes a member of the National Agriculture Editors Association and a judge at the Future Farmers of America convention in Kansas City.

Rollie sends him to Washington for a couple of days to spy on a trade association president before the Pfizer exec agrees to join its board. Bob fires the Leo Burnett ad agency out of Chicago after a twenty-five-year relationship because the division has become its smallest client, something he never wants to be. Dorn Communications out of Minneapolis now designs and prints *Agridynamics* and assists with the research conference. As a favor to Bob, Dorn commissions a study of the rabbit industry and agrees to produce a new magazine for the American Rabbit Breeders Association. Bob founds and edits the official magazine of the association. He also names it *Domestic Rabbits*, not telling anyone what the name will be for fear that it will take a long time at several board meetings to come up with any agreement.

Then he develops a publicity program as chairman of the advertising and publicity committee. Between the new magazine and the publicity, association membership soon doubles from eight to fifteen thousand, then doubles that. He runs for the board of directors and is elected as the youngest director in the organization's history.

When he attempts to add a commercial division, devoted to meat production, he rankles the rest of the ARBA board and the president because they irrationally fear hybrids will ruin the purebreds, forgetting that purebreds are required to make hybrids. He writes a series of magazine articles about meat production and the membership responds enthusiastically but the president fires him for it. The board votes to eliminate at-large directors, making each one responsible for a district. When Bob's term expires he decides to devote his time to promoting his book and writing another. The second one is called "Bob Bennett's Guide to Winning Rabbit Shows" and is published by Dorn.

Pfizer management decides to move ag division headquarters to Kansas City, a place Bob has no intention of living. After ten years with the company, which qualifies him for a pension, Bob decides to move himself elsewhere.

Chapter Thirty-four
Back to Vermont

Elsewhere means Vermont, to become the first marketing and sales director of Garden Way Publishing, with the major goal of selling books to non-bookstore retailers whose merchandise relates to, even matches company titles. Those goods include, of course, rabbit feed. After supporting sales and marketing for several years, Bob finally lands a line position with responsibility for the bottom line. With a higher salary and position than he had in New York, he also qualifies for awards of company stock. If he succeeds, he'll make much more than ever before. Sure, he had stock options at Pfizer, but in the Nixon era they never paid off. When they came due to exercise they cost more than what they were on the street.

Returning to Vermont long remained in the back of his mind— okay, maybe in the front. He thought it would be a much better place for the kids to grow up. Years earlier when the editorship of *Vermont Life* magazine opened upon the demise of Walter Hard, he applied. Well familiar with the state of course, he had also sold features and photos to the publication.

Because the job was offered but not at the salary he sought, he declined. Later he learned Dave Hakins earlier applied and was rejected. Bob never mentions he knows it to his friend.

The bride chooses blueprints for a two-story colonial designed by a nationally acclaimed Massachusetts architect. She also selects the Champlain lakeside town of Shelburne, primarily for its school. Her new home on a knoll will rise on over ten secluded open and wooded acres with a brook, okay, a rill, and pond, zoned agricultural-residential, protected by covenants that prohibit subdivision, only sixty-two miles north of her aged parents.

That's the upside.

Oh yes, there's another. Bob's successor in the ag division at Pfizer not only must live in Kansas City, he must die. It's a plane crash while on a business trip to Minnesota. Bob thinks hey that could have been me.

The downside? The bride misses New York and Bergen County shopping and son Bob becomes the new kid at school. Of the three kids, Bob takes it the toughest. Now a freshman at the Catholic high school, Rice Memorial, he becomes introverted and makes few friends, snobbishly deciding that all the Vermonters are hicks. The good part is that he buckles down to his studies and his marks shine. John is happy go lucky and makes a smooth transition. Alyssa misses her ballet teacher but her mother finds new ones and she is on her way to winning roles with the New York City Ballet in Saratoga Springs. She dances with Suzanne Farrell. George Balanchine pats her on the head. Her teary-eyed parents beam while watching her at the Saratoga Performing Arts Center. Alyssa makes friends with several of the adult dancers, who see her as a talented, beautiful and budding star as well as a sweet and endearing young lady.

How does Bob get the job at Garden Way? Ramsey Feed and Grain is the main reason although publisher Jack Williamson says he hires Bob to get him to stop writing letters about putting books in feed stores.

Nobody else really goes after non-bookstores. Oh, Ortho publishes books for hardware stores that sell their lawn and garden products. Sunset, in California, puts some gardening and landscaping titles in similar stores. These paperbacks all appear in the same format and all with 128 pages, regardless of the depth of the subject. The Garden Way books, content-driven, come in various sizes and page numbers. These obstacles will fall. The main thing on Bob's mind: the 12,000 bookstores are shrinking and sinking. They will drown with the advent of Amazon. Thanks to Bob and his vision, the publisher will write in 2016 that, more than two million people have picked up a *Storey's Guide to Raising Rabbits* at their local feed store.

Forty years in the future there will be only 1,200 bookstores and the publisher then will tell Bob his strategy saved the company. Now there are twice as many feed stores, thousands more hardware, lawn and garden, and other big box stores.

In truth, Williamson doesn't hire Bob. Lyman Wood, the CEO, the man who founded the company, realizes that his mail-order approach needs another string to its bow and is willing to take a flyer with the Pfizer guy. Williamson, a former bookstore traveler, devotes his efforts to those stores and thinks anything else is an accessory. He tells Bob his job is "special sales." Bob says all sales are special and while he's willing to do some commercial publishing on the side, he will make the non-book trade his objective and take the company where it's never been before. He will open accounts that can become outlets for the Troy-Bilt Tiller, the key product in the company. His long-term objective: become responsible for retail sales of the tiller and everything else the company sells by mail, which includes carts, work benches and cider presses, among other products.

It's not going to be easy. Bob visits Agway headquarters and meets the lawn and garden buyer, Howie Miller. Agway operates scores of stores in the northeast that serve big farmers and suburban backyard hobby types. Here's the buyer's response:

"I don't know you," Howie tells him. "I don't know your company and I don't know your books and I don't have time to read them and I am no expert so I won't know if they are any good even if I did. Not only that, the margin doesn't equal everything else we sell. So why should I buy from you?

"See ya."

Undeterred and a veteran of rejection, Bob hires an independent sales force, John H. Graham and Co. Inc., that sells time-tested products to Agway, such as Snap-Cut pruning shears and Allway tools. He finds the company back in New Jersey and makes a pal out of a young principal, Peter Goldsmith, a Garden Way book devotee. Pete accompanies Bob back to Syracuse and together they sit with Howie, who now agrees to take on the books, but only at their private trade show in the Catskills—a three-day affair where store managers congregate at booths with vendors and in the dining room of the resort hotel where they overeat lots of fattening food.

Many of the managers have heard of Garden Way through its direct marketing activity and like the idea and the orders pour in. It's the first big success but it comes only because Bob has found the salespeople who have made Agway happy for years. Internally, his sales challenge is just as big—he must get terms that meet the requirements of Agway and companies just like it. They don't care how good his product is—it must provide the profit they require or it doesn't get in the door. So it's 50 and 10 or 25 percent of the net, which Williamson swallows even though bookstores get only 50 off. The kicker: the books are non-returnable, unlike the book trade tradition.

With Graham aboard, Bob makes the kind of merchandisers the stores will take and comes up with a plan to offer them free. He builds the first one in his garage with hammer and saw but then gets a piece-work company employing the disabled to produce them. He charges twenty-five bucks for the display but throws in an equal value amount of free books. These of course cost the company only the printing cost because they are non-royalty titles produced in-house. He writes the sales lit including the catalog and mails it to his target wholesalers, primarily other ag co-ops like Agway, including Tractor Supply, Southern States, Wheat Belt and others across the country.

It's off to the trade shows—garden, hardware, farm supply and sporting goods. He adds wholesalers across the country and checks on other exhibitors to see what they are selling. At the National Hardware Show he sees rear-tine tillers. Some are Troy-Bilt knock-offs. Others come from overseas. Every one of them is benefiting from the Troy-Bilt advertising. Everyone except Troy-Bilt, which is paying to lose market share. Bob tells Lyman Wood that he's got to go two-step—put the tiller in the retail outlets he has opened with the books.

Wood won't do it. Jimmy Carter-era interest rates now reach double digits. Lyman craves an order with cash up front, then builds the machine. The two-step sales method requires borrowing to build and muttering 60 to 90 days about his money, all the while paying huge interest rates. It's not going to happen. Bob sees that his opportunity to head up a wholesale and retail sales operation is evaporating. He's not going to keep hoping. He's going to look elsewhere to increase his income.

The clincher comes when Wood wants to produce a reel-type lawnmower, which nobody uses except baseball fields and golf courses. Lyman keeps to his growth plan but the Troy guys want to keep the profits for their own pockets and a coup is brewing. The company may not last much longer.

Bob has a lot of stock cash coming. He's got three kids ready to go to college. The only way to get the cash he will need is to quit.

He takes the money and runs.

Chapter Thirty-five
Back to Rutland

He runs to Rutland.

In October 1981 Bob becomes director of corporate communications for Central Vermont Public Service Corporation in Rutland. It's a 62-mile commute down Route 7. He buys a new diesel Rabbit, good for better than fifty miles per gallon, replacing his rundown sixty-three Beetle, which never would survive this demanding daily grind. He leaves Shelburne at six-thirty, so he's in the office at eight, ten minutes early. Of course, this is October. When it snows he will start sooner.

CVPS pays more than what he earned at Garden Way, which is good because son Bob starts at the University of Vermont. The bride remains a stay-at-home mom who will maintain that status until Alyssa starts high school three years from now. Son John is a high school freshman. College cash will be needed for him before long. Garden Way stock proceeds will supplement the salary and pay the profs.

Bob settles into the northeast corner office facing Grove Street that once was occupied by Robert Noble, who sold him his first pair of New Zealand Reds and served as his counselor for the Rabbit

Raising merit badge. His staff includes Pat Slattery, younger brother of Jack, a classmate since sixth grade. A former *Herald* reporter, Pat writes news releases and deals with the media. Hypochondriac Ted Pendleton works on advertising and edits the company newspaper, the *Circuit*. There's young Mary Ellen ("Emmy"), a writer, and Mary Jane ("Emjay"), the veteran secretary. Bob reports to Tom Hurcomb, VP external affairs.

Lots of people claim power company execs simply stuff customers' rate checks into their pockets. So it becomes Bob's job to try to change that perception. If he does, when the company seeks even higher rates from the public service board it will face little or no consumer opposition.

Of course he cannot change the rates that people hate. But what he can do is produce reasons to like the company and balance or mitigate the perception.

Hurcomb and his marketing manager Dick Kopsack strive to sell water heater insulation jackets for $25 but few sell even though they are supposed to save twice that amount every year. They sell for $15 in hardware stores. So Bob promotes them at company cost of $10 with television commercials he writes and directs with a Burlington production company. They sell like the proverbial hotcakes and Bob backs up the sales with news releases that tell how much money customers are saving. Now the company can buy in greater volume at a lower price, which covers the tv spots. Bob explains to Hurcomb that public relations requires the company actually to *do* something for the public; then publicity can trumpet the results.

But that's only the beginning. Bob surveys the employees. They think the name "public service" actually means they should do some public service. Imagine that. What would they like to do? Feed the hungry. Right now the local Jewish, Catholic and Protestant clergy have food shelves. The idea is that their congregations should bring a can or box of food to services. Then volunteers will make it available to those in need.

The problem, however, is that fewer and fewer people are attending religious services in Vermont, the least religious state in the nation. And when they do, in the rush to get the family dressed and ready in time, they seldom remember to take anything. Also, the hungry are often too embarrassed to go to the church for food.

Bob concocts a plan called "Share With a Hungry Vermonter," featuring receptacle boxes in supermarkets. The infamous criminal Willie Sutton said he robbed banks because that's where the money is. The store, not the church or synagogue is where the food is of course. A Plattsburgh television station will promote it if he will call it "Share With a Hungry Neighbor." Boxes now also fill up in Empire State supermarkets.

Meanwhile, Bob makes his mark as a financial writer, turning out corporate annual reports that win the top awards in the electric utility and *Financial World* magazine contests, with the latter finding him in New York in tuxedo to accept a plaque. He does so well with the reports, which hardly anybody else wants to write, that the company pays him a handsome contract rate to keep writing them for several years after he leaves.

Commuting one hundred twenty-four miles a day gets old. Bob and the bride look at several homes in Rutland and the area. But Rutland has lost some luster. So after seven years in Rutland it is time to look elsewhere.

Preferably close to home.

Chapter Thirty-six
Another Dutch Treat

The back seat of the well-traveled VW hatchback sags under son Bob's tv set, video recorder, stereo, two electric guitars, an electric typewriter, books, records, tapes, bedspread, sheets, pillow and suitcase—everything the kid thinks he needs to begin three years at Union University's Albany Law School, 160 miles south of their Shelburne home.

As the dad heads down Route 7 in the 70-degree September sunshine, his thoughts return to another Saturday, 27 years earlier when he was his son's age, 22. That's when as an airman, he was assigned to temporary duty at Ellington Air Force Base, the one that became the Houston Space Center. He thinks back to phoning his father, stationed at Fort Hood, and how he hadn't seen him for half his life, back when he was ll. The two of them went to Galveston in the shiny Ford Skyliner for a shore dinner. And his father said, "Let's go Dutch."

If that wasn't just like him, Bob thought then and now. After 22 years and all the dough he made as a major and me a lowly enlisted man looking to the end of his first and last hitch so he can work his way through college.

Dutch.

He couldn't believe it then and he can't believe it now.

Clearly, he can't forget it either.

Driving Bob to law school makes him smile. He has wanted to be the kind of father you could depend on. After urging Bob to study from grade and junior high through high school and even the first year of college before he really buckled down, here he is going to law school and his dad is driving him there.

This is s-a-t-i-s-f-a-c-t-i-o-n!!!

It will be an enjoyable drive. They will move him in and dad will be back home by mid-afternoon.

Not quite.

Suddenly the temperature gauge lurches to the right, just a notch from the red.

Damn.

Worse.

Three weeks earlier the head blew on the hundred-thousand-mile engine. Two days after being rebuilt the water pump split in the rain twenty-six miles from home. The dealer towed it to Rutland, where Bob still worked at CVPS, and replaced the pump.

Defective, the mechanic said.

The new one lasted three days.

Defective, the mechanic said.

A third replacement leaks under the hood now. Bob pulls to the shoulder for a look. The coolant tank, nearly bone dry, drips to turn the blacktop green. After suffering with the problem so often lately, Bob keeps a jug of coolant in the car. He pours some in, turns the heater on full blast, opens the windows wide and nurses the crate five miles to a garage in Middlebury.

The owner supplies no water pump of course but says a fan relay switch will take the car thirty-five miles south to Rutland where the dealer will, Bob hopes, have still another water pump that he can install quickly.

Who wants to unpack all the kid's stuff and cram it into a rental car?

"Just top the tank with coolant before you get to Brandon, and you'll make it because the fan will come on if the engine gets too hot. Better tell them you want a new water pump this time. No more of that rebuilt stuff."

The needle nearly rubs the red mark but they make it to the dealership before noon.

"Another water pump? It will take a couple of hours," the service manager says. By now they know each other too well.

"You guys should be able to put one in pretty fast by now," Bob tells him with a forced smile. "Even blindfolded. I've got to get this kid to Albany and we haven't got all day." Bob is angry but doesn't want to get the service manager mad, so that's all he says. Wimpiness, he thinks, sometimes is the better part of valor.

"We'll get it done as soon as we can."

The two planned to stop in Rutland anyway to pick up some photos the son has ordered. Bob suggests lunch while waiting for the car.

"How about a grinder at Gill's? You've heard me rave about them for years. You pay for the enlargements. By the way, you owe me $5.20 for developing the film. But one of those prints is for the house, for the insurance company, so that's $3. You still owe me $2.20."

"Tell you what," he says, "I'll buy the grinders and we're even."

"We'll order just one," Bob says, "a large, cut in half. You couldn't eat the whole thing anyway. At least I can't."

The grinder is $2.85—$3.85 with two sodas. Bob lets the kid buy. The car is ready by one forty-five, with a hundred miles to go.

The needle starts out where it should and to nervous Bob's absolute amazement it stays there until four when they drive down New Holland Avenue and pull into Albany Law School.

All the kid's stuff necessitates six trips up the elevator to his fifth-floor room, which looks out onto a football field. Who's field? His son doesn't know but couldn't resist saying: "Law school doesn't play football, for crying out loud."

"Okay," Bob tells him. "We made it. I'm heading home. After you get settled call your mother. Tell her that with the same luck we have had since Rutland I'll be home about eight. She'll want to know you got here okay and how your room is and everything."

"And if you need anything," the dad feels compelled to add, before the son cuts him off.

"God, I think I'm going to jump out the window if you give me a big speech."

But Bob persists.

"Look, if you need any dough or anything, remember, you've got a father. That's what they are for." And he shakes his son's hand.

"Okay, okay. You'd better get going."

The needle remains in its rightful place and Bob reaches home in less than three hours. On the way he recalls the shore dinner in Texas and the grinder at Gill's. Hell, he thinks, I made Bob buy lunch today without even trying and it didn't bother me a bit.

I guess you could say we went Dutch.

Chapter Thirty-seven
A Big Raise in Burlington

The Howard Bank in Burlington needs a new vice president of corporate communications and marketing. Bob admits little knowl-
edge of banking. He has never even had a checking account. His
signature on a joint account would be as unseen as invisible ink. He
never sees or signs one. The bride keeps the only checkbook. Ever
the accountant, she keeps the books and pays all the bills. Bob, as he
has done since they wed, simply delivers his salary to the bride. His
only personal funds come from royalties and other writing fees. Plus
the rabbit business.

He does, however, feel confident of his experience in corporate
communications, with its internal and external facets, and public
relations plus advertising, sales and marketing. The prospect of becoming a bank officer with a staff of five, reporting to the president,
with a seat at the table with the executive committee, a furnished
walnut paneled office and a $10,000 increase in pay, all with a simple
10-minute commute, sounds pretty good. His well-crafted resume
wins him a smooth interview with the president and the job.

He gives Hurcomb a two-week notice but maintains his membership in the company credit union, where he planted the proceeds of the

Garden Way stock. The interest rate in the money market fund is still pretty high. This time he can thank Jimmy Carter. Bob's heir-apparent, newly hired, presents him with a French Opinel folding pocketknife. Then Bob drives the diesel VW up Route 7 to Governors Lane.

The first morning at the bank, a Monday, almost matches the one on his first day at Mobil Oil on 42nd Street. That was when Libyan Gaddafi nationalized the company oil fields and facilities, prompting calls from all the financial and other news media in New York. This day it goes the other way. Over the weekend the bank president dies of a heart attack and Bob must recount his long career in an obit news release. Having met him only briefly, in the job interview, much research in jig time is required. And then there is the announcement of the successor, his new boss, who did not hire him, whom he has never met.

That's Bill Chadwick and it would be better if he never had.

Chadwick is hell-bent on selling the bank and pocketing a big company stock payday. He begins by sacking his high-priced officers, one by one, as he cuts costs to improve the bottom line. These are guys who evaluate moves by their staffs but really do very little of monetary value. Meanwhile, Bob actually produces. He writes and manages the annual report, making sure Chadwick likes his own photo, the key to success. Bob wins another *Financial World* magazine contest and he goes to New York in black tie to accept a plaque. He comes up with a scheme to save the bacon of the Visa department by acquiring Sabra Field art for a Vermont Classic Visa Card, which includes a charitable donation for every transaction. The manager of the department, which had been a candidate for dissolution, becomes a senior vice president.

Bob also produces collateral material, making certain the front-line tellers have input and approve of the final product. It coincides with his advertising and publicity. He comes up with an internal sales program and meeting and engineers the annual meeting, but sweats it out because Chadwick is drunk as a skunk.

He edits the employee newsletter and all goes well until Chadwick decides to write a message asking the staff to be more careful in their daily work to avoid mistakes. Bob protests it as a bad idea but examines the ill-advised message and gets Chadwick, his secretary and the members of his own staff to scrutinize it. Of course, it carries a typo anyway and employees snicker up their sleeves and enjoy it at lunchtime. Some of them phone the CEO to point out the goof. Bill fumes. He calls Bob on the carpet.

The newsletter says "noboby's perfect."

Instead of saying he told him not to write it Bob tells him no Billy's perfect either.

Meanwhile, Chadwick continues to micromanage the budget, seeking ways to make the bank look more profitable. He'd like to unload Bob and his hefty salary, but knows he needs him to create the quarterly and annual financial reports. But he strikes a deal with his communications and marketing vice president. If Bob will resign, Bill will pay him six months' salary and insurance and retain him for the financial reports at an hourly rate greater than his annual salary. That he can do by cutting other areas of the consultant budget and by hiring a young successor for less money. After only a couple of years as a banker, Bob jumps at the deal.

Chapter Thirty-eight
His Own Boss

How difficult is it to begin his own business? Not very. He makes more money than ever with the birth of The Bennett Company, a Vermont Subchapter S corporation. In a basement office he built himself down there years ago for writing books, he's fully equipped. For two years now the power company pays him $80 an hour plus expenses to write and produce its annual financial reports because nobody there knows how or wants to try. Besides, the power company headquarters sits sixty-eight miles south of the only printer who can produce the book.

For Bob, in Shelburne, reaching Burlington designers and printers takes only ten minutes. That's more significant than the miles because page proofs require scrutiny at all hours of the night to make the publication deadline. The company need not buy lodging for anyone else. Bob, from home, is on the job.

The key challenge: keeping up. Sometimes he seems like the vaudeville guy who spins several plates spinning on vertical sticks

His pal Dave Hakins, who now runs a sports travel business in New Jersey, retains Bob to write sales brochures and ads for the Wall Street Journal and Popular Mechanics magazine for his various trips.

These include the Super Bowl, Indianapolis 500, the Final Four, the World Series and a cruise to Alaska. Of course, Bob brought him to Pfizer so it seems a bargain that now he works for Dave.

His contacts with area graphic artists pay off. Their clients need copywriters and refer them to Bob. Another big way to get business: to reply to want ads by companies that need in-house marketing, advertising and public relations help. Experienced Bob helps them immediately on a professional contractual basis until they find an employee—or on a part-time retainer basis for less than the price of a full-time rookie.

Two nursing homes seek a marketing director. Bob persuades the administrator to hire him at full-time pay for part time. He writes resident manuals and recruits private pay residents. Champlain College needs an adjunct marketing instructor. Bob teaches there for a couple of years. One kid dons a backwards baseball cap in the classroom and refuses to doff it. Bob declares the class over if the cap remains on his scalp. The lad looks around the room at the disapproving stares and caves.

Real estate agents pay him to photograph their model condos and produce their portfolios. It all comes down to keeping the plates spinning. Bob wonders why he didn't start doing this years ago. He had learned the ins and outs of publicity, publishing, advertising, marketing, financial relations and sales. It all results from writing and photography ability. So Bob does it all and in the eighties he makes eighty thou the first year, ten grand more than he made at the bank. He does more in a day in his home office than he ever did in a company job. He works almost every waking minute of every day including weekends and holidays and he couldn't be happier.

But Mrs. Charming and Dependable does not share his enthusiasm, daily reminding him that he is not spending much time with her and neglecting home maintenance and repairs. Money isn't everything, except for law school and undergraduate college expenses for three offspring. It may not be everything, but it seems like everyone wants some of it. Yes, she's working for the acclaimed neurosurgeon Nancy Binter and pulling down a good salary as her office manager. So if money isn't everything why is he driving a VW Rabbit with a quarter of a million miles on the odometer?

So he soldiers on, this man of the family, pulling in more accounts. Then one day he and pal Dave Hakins pitch the National Gardening Association for a garden trip to England. They would promote it in the monthly association gardening magazine. The association decides not to do it, but some of its employees like what Bob has to say. They remember his sales success at Garden Way Publishing.

He's offered the new position of advertising director for the magazine. Full time.

It's the new position because the magazine carries no paid advertising. What it does carry is offers for merchandise for gardeners that began life as the Garden Way Country Kitchen Catalog. Will Raap ran the catalog and when Garden Way collapsed, he moved his wares to the magazine. The association would like to sell it all to Raap, and he would like to buy it because he wants to turn it into an operation that one day will become Gardeners Supply Company, a very large mail order and brick and mortar business. The magazine can't carry ads from competing companies with Raap's stuff in it and would rather bolster its income with ad sales. It's a win-win for both Will and the association.

So Bob begins to build a sales force and a sales plan. Remembering that editorial and advertising are like church and state, he designs a plan based on demographics, one that has nothing to do with editorial content. He knows he can't control content and that it has little to do with sales. With the help of the research director, Bruce Butterfield, he discovers what gardeners are likely to buy. It's not all garden related. For example, he sells several roofing shingle companies advertising because gardeners are older people in their own homes, ready for a roofing job

He sets sales goals for each issue and bargains a bonus deal with David Els, the executive director. They hit the goal every issue and Bob and his staff pocket extra cash. Some of the salespeople are in-house, but Bob hires commission sales reps for the Midwest, south and west coast. Bob knows how to operate at trade shows and takes the magazine staff to Chicago for the Hardware Show, to Louisville for the Outdoor Power Equipment Show and to various other venues in quest of advertisers. It pays off. It's not all work, because Bob knows how to play the trade show game. For example, in Chicago, at the end of the day, he eschews the traffic on Lake Shore Drive for a pause at McCormick Inn. A walk down any hallway leads to a company suite, with comestibles (big on shrimp and bacon-wrapped scallops), a bar and merchandise giveaways. It's for the company customers of course but nobody checks I.D. After the cocktail hour, when the traffic on Lake Shore Drive subsides, it's off to Chicago Bears Mike Ditka's restaurant for a big buffet—complimentary of course.

He also makes a lot of contacts, including "America's Master Gardener," Jerry Baker, whose books include "Plants Are Like People." Jerry loves to point out that if you eat a carrot you must be a cannibal, so why be a vegetarian when you are so indicted. He meets some celebrities, including Dodgers slugger Frank Howard who says "It's nice to be remembered," and famous skater Peggy Fleming, who tells him "How come you never told me you had a crush on me?"

After five years of success running an ad sales department, the circulation declines. That's because David Els decides to do two detrimental things. He siphons off add revenue for ill-advised education programs instead of using it to build circulation.

Advertisers now pay less per thousand, and income declines.

As does the bonus.

So Bob decides to quit, although Els suggests he stay part time at a reduced salary and also serve his Bennett Company clients from his National Gardening office. He thinks about it, but the next day he goes to his Governors Lane mailbox and standing there is neighbor Bob Kelly.

Chapter Thirty-nine
Buy a Business?

Bob Kelly has sold his share of the Burlington CPA firm he founded. He buys out a client, a former Catholic priest iconographer who began a mail order business to sell reproductions—wood plaques, posters and greeting cards—even refrigerator magnets. Kelly kept the company books and liked what he saw. So when the ex-priest decided to sell out and move west to write icons full time, Kelly became the owner of Bridge Building Images.

Kelly wants to build the business but an accountant needs sales and marketing assistance. Bob will help and if he likes its looks there is the potential to buy the company. Bob decides to investigate. The inventory includes traditional Roman Catholic, Eastern Rite and Orthodox images of Christ, the Virgin Mary and assorted saints but also a variety of potential saints and other ancient and recent personages sporting bogus halos, suggesting they are among the canonized.

Others are fanciful, pretentious creations done as native Americans. Current customers, many of them religious and spiritual liberals, are thrilled with the fanciful renditions. Potential buyers, traditional conservative Catholics or Greek Orthodox, are disgusted,

calling them sacrilegious. To complicate matters, Kelly, a Congrega-
tionalist, does not appreciate the difference, having no background
in either of the other religions or art. All he really understands is the
bottom line. And now he has a better grasp of the expenses entailed,
which leads him to reduce his sales promotion costs.

Kelly needs a marketer with a parochial school background;
somebody who knows saints and appreciates liturgical art.

That's Bob.

The first thing to do of course is sell what you have. The next
thing is to find out what your customers want and supply them. The
first don't sell very well and the second is difficult because the ex-
priest iconographer won't produce what a potentially larger base of
customers wants. He wants to make what he wants.

Which they don't.

With better catalogs and a website Bob begins to increase sales of
the inventory. Then he finds that Kelly doesn't really own the rights to
most of the images, those by the fallen-away priest. He has only a ver-
bal agreement. So Bob encourages Kelly to contract with other iconog-
raphers, which works well for a while until the former cleric decides to
pull his images and start his own company with its own website.

And to sue Kelly.

So the whole thing is a mess and Bob decides he's not going to
pursue the possibility of buying the business. He has now reached
retirement age, gets Social Security payments to supplement his salary, investments, a Pfizer pension and his book royalties.

While he ponders his next move, the Lynn brothers, owners of
one daily and several weekly newspapers, want an editor-publisher
for the weekly community *Essex Reporter*. Bob decides to take the
job on a one-year basis while the incumbent goes to Europe. Bob is
back in the newspaper business.

He tells Kelly he'll return next year.

Heading up the weekly means supervising a managing editor, a staff writer, a layout artist and a secretary/receptionist. Bob is the ad salesman and the editorial writer. There are part-time reporters and a photographer. High school kids do the deliveries. And there are Apple computers—nothing Bob has ever dealt with, being a Windows guy. Printing takes place in St. Albans, home of the St. Albans Messenger.

Bob sells more ads than the paper ever had. He finally gets the hang of the McIntosh and of QuickBooks to pay the salaries, the fees and to record expenses and revenue. He covers police and local government and schools. It's a fast-paced situation but Bob is more than equal to the task—except for the editorials. The Lynn brothers want him to expound on national issues. Bob leaves those to the nation's dailies, preferring to discuss local issues. He takes a conservative approach to those, which irks the owners, liberals through and through.

After a year of this, with ad sales up and a new editor/publisher in the wings, Bob returns to Bridge Building.

Chapter Forty
Bob the Builder

Bob always pursues something on the side. Jobs while in school. Civilian jobs in the Air Force. Photography, including book photos, weddings, publicity and selling stories and photos to *Vermont Life* magazine and the *Vermont Catholic Tribune* while at the *Herald*. Freelance journal editing, articles to Sunday magazine sections, and of course the book writing and the rabbit business. Plus serving all the clients who kept pursuing him while with the power company, the bank and National Gardening.

As if that were not enough to keep him busy, he is a builder. There is the grandfather clock and assorted Queen Anne furniture, including a butler's tray table, candlestand, mirror, sideboard, Pennsylvania lowboy, curio cabinet, corner chair and more. Plus the built-in cabinets and bookshelves, the mantle, the chair rails and crown molding woodwork, the window seat.

He built the barn from garage plans and a greenhouse from salvaged windows and doors. When you come right down to it, he leads a double life. It could be partly Baldy Brand's fault, because his Godfather familiarized him with carpenter's tools.

When their daughter is due to marry in a year, her mother finally insists on a sunroom. A bridesmaids tea demands just such a setting. Or so the mother of the bride-to-be insists. Bob builds a scale model that wins approval.

He decides to incorporate it with an adjacent covered porch and a mudroom/vestibule and finds a contractor who agrees to do the job—as soon as he finishes building a porch in Burlington. Meanwhile, he tells Bob to order and pay for the lumber and other materials on his contractor account and that he will simply bill for time. With piles of studs, sheathing and assorted other boards, cement for the concrete footings and shingles for the roof all sitting in the driveway, Bob waits for the contractor. And waits. And waits. A lumberyard clerk reveals that the contractor has completed the Burlington porch and bolted to Bermuda with a girlfriend. No telling when he'll return.

So Bob decides to do the job himself.

He's sixty-six years old now and walks the two-football field driveway to his mailbox. Halfway back he stops, finding himself short of breath. He reports this situation to the bride. She says go see a doctor. Of course, he has no doctor, having last seen one back in New Jersey, some thirty years earlier, for poison ivy contracted while picking blackberries in Bermuda shorts, a really stupid idea. Bleeding scratches attacked by poison ivy sent him for cortisone shots. See a doctor? He will think about it.

Envisioning a backhoe destroying his lawn, Bob decides to excavate eleven four-foot holes for concrete footings by hand with a clamshell digger. The three-day Memorial Day weekend looms. He tells the bride he thinks being sixty-six makes him short of breath but after he digs the footing holes if he still feels tired he'll make an appointment.

So he digs all eleven and decides to see Dr. Fink in Shelburne. Fink takes his blood pressure, thought high by the ophthalmologist who laser-treated a burst blood vessel in his right eye. The doc sends him to a clinic for a stress test. The cardiologist says three arteries are eighty percent blocked. Without a stent he'll be dead by September.

The sunroom will have to wait—not for a stent but a triple bypass that puts him out of commission from June until September, when he knows he has recuperated because the bride tells him to pick up his own damn socks. He finally goes back to Bridge Building and the holes in the ground. It's still warm enough to pour the footings and he completes the deck for the sunroom, vestibule-mud room and porch.

During the winter the bride and bride-to-be remind him the sunroom must be completed before Memorial Day, the date of the wedding. If he gets it done it will be a just a year since he dug those holes and had his chest split open like a lobster.

The work is fun, even more than he had when building the barn. The sunroom goes up, roofed and painted and a prefinished hardwood floor goes down in time for the tea party. Alyssa marries Christopher Igo, a magnificent choice, but not surprising because she and her mother have been eyeing candidates and planning a wedding since the day she was born. Alyssa selects St. Joseph's Co-Cathedral in Burlington because local St. Catherine's doesn't offer an aisle of great train length, suitable for a sterling "here comes the bride." Then there's the Shelburne Farms Coach Barn reception which costs God only knows how much. The father of the bride salutes both mothers for producing outstanding specimens to carry the family in the future. The Igos then fly off to the fabled Amalfi Coast of Italy.

Afterwards Bob spends the rest of the summer evenings and weekends building the porch and the mudroom/vestibule. Then he adds a bluestone patio and walk and steps and perennial bed along it to complete the picture and turn the backyard into something better looking than a Wiffle ball field.

Back indoors the following fall he decides to remodel the kitchen with its dark pine cabinets and a round maple table that takes up too much room. What he has in mind are maple cabinets and an island with needed storage to replace the table. All will be in a cream paint color and so will be the adjacent family room, separated only by an archway and half wall. His idea of a color scheme lightens everything and ties it all together.

New cabinets and a fancy island would look great and cost several thousand dollars. Bob decides to buy unfinished maple doors and European hidden cup hinges, plus moldings to dress up the cabinets. Then he buys two unfinished base cabinets, bolts them together and fashions a maple top from boards he glues and clamps and stains and waxes. Then he buys four unfinished bar-height chairs and stains them to match the island top. To dress up the sides of all the cabinets he adds moldings and the original pine doors, which are of the same design as the maple ones. He paints everything with foam brushes to produce an unblemished finish. It results in a brand-new kitchen for about eleven hundred dollars and a resounding triumph because:

The bride says she loves it.

He decides to keep building. Of course a man cave. He already partitioned and outfitted an office in the basement. Now new risers and treads redo the stairs. They flank a hallway with a closet and a bench. He wires and finishes a pine-paneled room, ideal for a big screen television and plenty of shelves for books on baseball, gardening, fishing and favorite novelists. He builds in the shelves and fashions a fancy lighted ceiling that hides the soil pipe running through the middle. He lays down a floor of individual vinyl planks and when son Bob sees them he says he thought you couldn't put hardwood on a concrete floor.

The television, standing on a cabinet built into the wall, completes the picture—except for all the pictures he hangs on the walls. He rubs his hands together with relish.

But that's not the real satisfaction.

Chapter Forty-one
The Real Satisfaction

There is no denying it, Bob derives a lot of satisfaction out of his work. He longed to be a newspaper reporter and editor and loved it. He ached to be a public relations and advertising guy and liked it almost as much. He sought to sell and he sold. He wanted to write books and he published. And of course he wished for college and went to three, quitting only after a master's degree and before completing a doctorate strictly for a chance to be a Little League coach.

But none of that matched the thrill and satisfaction of winning Miss Charming and Dependable and helping her raise three fabulous children. Being semi-fatherless, he wanted to be a good dad. He tried very hard. He keeps trying and thinks that the children prove that some of his efforts paid off.

Their mother, beautiful and brilliant, is a fabulous role model who steers the family ship. Besides her great mothering and housekeeping, this financial guru who seems to Bob to blow a lot of dough actually keeps everything solvent and in style. Her accomplishments are classic and would take another book to describe fully. But you can get a glimpse of them in the children.

First son Bob, who arrived on a rainy morning in January, becomes a lawyer and the head of his own firm. On the way he becomes an author of two published books and a libertarian politician who wins more state legislature votes than anyone else in his party while both a candidate and a college boy. John, early in a school for the gifted, becomes an outstanding teacher after achieving the highest Scholars Bowl score in the nation in the national championships, and later coaches his own team to a state title. Their baby sister dances for George Balanchine in ballets with the best company in the world, the New York City Ballet, bringing tears to Bob's eyes at Saratoga Springs New York, after winning a national dance competition in Manhattan. Then she tops it off by becoming an executive with General Electric and producing two outstanding grandchildren (who would require yet another book). All three kids earned the post-high school educations Bob yearned as an Air Force enlisted man—one of the greatest satisfactions of all. That included undergraduate and master's and doctor of laws degrees, completed without student loans or any other debt on their part (but with old cars for twelve years on Bob's and the bride's).

So, in 2003, it's time to take monetary advantage of the brilliance of his boys. He sits in the family room with the two of them on the day after Christmas, talking about baseball books they all received as gifts from each other.

"How come," Bob asks his sons, "nobody has ever written a book about Johnny Podres?"

A diehard Dodgers fan, Bob's all-time favorite Dodger is Podres, the first and only Brooklyn pitcher to defeat the New York Yankees in the World Series. It happened in 1955 after Bob suffered through losses to the Yanks in the '40s and '50s, the days of his youth. But Podres made all the pain go away in 1955.

Bob had interviewed him in the winter of 1961. It followed Johnny's eighteen-win season when he made his annual trip to Rutland with his bowling team for a match with locals and a dinner at the Italian American Club on Grove Street, next door to Central Vermont Public Service Corporation headquarters. Bob tells the sports editor about the visit and so on a Sunday walks over to the club with Aldo Merusi's Speed Graphic, where Podres sips beer and twirls spaghetti with the winners and losers.

"It's a family newspaper," he tells the pitcher, "so I'd like a picture without the beer bottle. How about holding a coffee cup?"

Podres reluctantly cooperates and Bob clicks the shutter button. Nothing. No flash. Beads of sweat invade his forehead. He tries again, pulling the dark slide on the other side of his first film holder.

Nothing.

He's up to bat in his most important game and so far he's swinging and missing.

More sweat.

Podres is getting antsy.

Fortunately, Bob recalls that spit on the flashbulb can ignite it and so on his third try he blasts the flash gun at the table.

"Before I go John," Bob tells him, "I've got to say you that you are my all-time favorite Dodger for what you did in '55, so I'd love to get your autograph."

The genial John plucks the wad of copy paper from Bob's sports jacket pocket, scribbles on it and puts it back. Bob returns to the office and the darkroom and success—a good shot will run on the sports page.

Still living at home with his mother he excitedly tells her that night that he has met his hero and has his autograph but cannot show it to her because this is what the pitcher wrote:

"For Bob Bennett, the best fxxxxxxx photographer in the world. Johnny Podres."

Fifty years later Bob recalls that meeting but of course the pitcher does not. He finds that out when he calls Johnny up. His hero lives only one hundred miles away by the highway, if not as the crow flies, which it could easily do across the lake from Shelburne to Queensbury, New York, where the pitcher lives with Joanie, his wife, a former Ice Follies performer.

Bob gets him on the phone and says he wants to write his biography.

"Forget it," Podres says. "A whole bunch of guys have wanted to do that. I ain't got time. I don't care about it. Right now I'm getting ready to go to spring training with the Phillies so I won't be around anyway."

So Bob says how about I'll call you back when spring training is over and I'll come over and we'll talk about it.

"Okay, so give me a call but don't expect much. I really don't have the time for this."

At the beginning of April the pitching coach is back in Queensbury and agrees to meet Bob.

"I'll see you at the gas station on the other side of Exit 22 on the Northway."

Bob appears there, follows Podres a few blocks to his home and opens his car door, revealing a gallon of Vermont maple syrup.

"Oh," the pitcher declares, "you've got the good stuff!"

Inside the split level in a quiet, '60s-developed neighborhood, Bob meets the attractive blonde Joan, the former Ice Follies skater, who greets him warmly. For years she has wished Johnny would agree to a biography, but he has spurned the best sports writers, mostly because he realized they all wanted to make some money on his time. Podres, the consummate pro, is all about money. He never made much as a player for the Dodgers, somewhat more as a pitching coach for the Phillies, Red Sox, Tigers and Padres and he's suspicious, but he graciously shows Bob his living room trophies and photos, including the World Series MVP trophy from 1955, when he won the greatest fall classic ever played. And the Sportsman of the Year cup from *Sports Illustrated*.

Settling in his living room, Johnny is glad to hear that Bob is a Catholic who hates the Second Vatican Council, and is a conservative Republican, slightly to the right of Genghis Khan. Then it's down to business. Bob tells John that he's published seven books, that son Bob has published two and that son John has been published in anthologies. He tells Johnny the three of them would work on this title and that they would split royalties with him—half to Johnny and the other half divided among the co-authors.

When he learns that he might make some money on the effort, he agrees, and Bob presents him with a contract, pointing out that son Bob is a lawyer.

Joan is pleased. John shows little emotion, but Bob soon learns he hardly ever does. Johnny Podres is all business. Affable but serious. Does he remember when Bob photographed him at the Rutland Italian American Club? No. Does he recall the inscription and autograph he wrote on the note paper? No. But he agrees to be interviewed at his house on Saturday mornings throughout the spring and summer.

And then the phone rings.

It's Al "the bull" Ferrara, calling from California. An esteemed former teammate, he wants to know which horse to bet on at Santa Anita. Then the phone rings again. It's Don Zimmer, also a teammate and manager of the Red Sox who hired Johnny to be his pitching coach. He's in Florida. They have a history with horses that dates to 1953 when they met at Ebbets Field. He needs to know how to place his bets at Hialeah. Johnny spends hours reading the Racing Form and placing wagers on the phone with New York off-track betting. He bets in the morning, glued to afternoon television for results. One of his two sons drives sulkies at Saratoga Raceway. The other pounds sidewalks for the post office. Neither played pro ball.

The phone will interrupt every Saturday morning all through the summer while Bob and John and son Bob interview the pitcher. It will almost always be Zimmer.

Bob wants the book to stick to on-the-field baseball. Son Bob wants to include off-the-field off-color adventures, of which there were many. They argue often but only one four-letter word gets in and that one is during play on the field. Meanwhile son John contacts and interviews players and others who impacted John's life (or he impacted theirs).

At the same time, Bob deals with a major sports book publisher who agrees to put it in print.

Bob sends chapters as they are completed. The editor likes them but returns no contract. It turns out he won't publish it for another year, not the fiftieth anniversary of the Podres killing of the Yankees in 1955. Having been strung along, Bob decides he must self-publish to get it out by spring of '55. Only later does he find out that the publisher has already agreed to publish Marty Allen's "Brooklyn Remembered," which covers the same '55 series but not specifically on Podres. Allen had written several other books for him and was owed some allegiance.

So they pay to publish a hard cover edition of "Johnny Podres, Brooklyn's Only Yankee Killer," but it pays off big time. Not only do they profit on the self-published edition, it gets picked up and republished in soft cover trade paperback by Rooftop Publishing and they continue to make money on over 20,000 copies sold, in both editions, not bad for a baseball book considering there are so many out there on the bookshelves. Podres likes the royalties too, but it gets more lucrative at book signing venues.

Spending time at Podres' place is a kick but watching him down a dozen donuts at the kitchen table every Saturday morning while chain smoking Camels is disconcerting, along with Zimmer's phone calls. I mean, here he is hanging out with his boyhood hero, his all-time favorite Dodger.

And worrying about him.

Chapter Forty-two

Can You Believe It?

They drive down the Northway and the New York Thruway, for Johnny Podres Day in Brooklyn. Bob sits on the front seat of the Caddy, but he feels like he's on a bench in the bullpen.

Some little boys dream of becoming a big-league baseball player. Bob gave that one up early. He was called Robert by his teachers and his mother when she was stern. Earlier he was Bobby but he outgrew that toddler moniker. The only other Roberts called Bobby were pro athletes, e.g. Bobby Thomson, Bobby Orr and others.

Brooklyn lies miles ahead, but Bob has arrived. On this road trip, the pitcher, as if anointing him a big leaguer, calls him Bobby.

Podres drives as if he knows his way around the borough, which of course he does. First stop, a bank on Montague Street, the former location of the Brooklyn Dodgers front office. The bank invites its high roller customers to a cocktail party and book signing with a chance to meet and greet Johnny, the borough's biggest hero, who as a 23-year-old brought the borough of Brooklyn a degree of respectability beyond its wildest dreams. The bank has bought five hundred books for its customers, including matronly members of a teenage girl fan club who bring photos of their pep rallies to Johnny to see and sign.

Bob and son Bob, known on the book cover as Robert S., flank the living legend at a table loaded with books. It's a delighted passel of bank patrons, and Johnny holds forth signing books and photos brought by dozens of mid-twentieth century Brooklyn Dodgers devotees who shower their hero with adulation. It's a glorious night of nostalgia and some fans say they would have elected the kid pitcher the president of the borough if he were on the ballot.

Among them, a Yankees fan taunts Johnny, reminding him that in fifty-six Don Larsen tossed a perfect World Series game at the Dodgers.

"I was in the Navy then," Podres replies with a big smile. "But if I was on the mound against Larsen, you can be sure I would have matched him pitch for pitch and that game might still be going on."

The next morning Bob and Robert S. join the pitcher at the New York Board of Trade on Wall Street where a hundred books sell for fifty dollars each with half going to charity. After a lunch with the manager of the Heisman Trophy ceremony, who organized the New York festivities, it's off to Long Island for a Johnny Podres Golf Tournament, with hundreds of fans and former teammates, including hurler Ralph Branca and catcher Joe Pignatano. Major sponsor The Dime Bank of Brooklyn purchases books for all the golfers and supplies 1955 inscribed Brooklyn Dodgers caps to all in attendance. Podres, known to avoid every opportunity for a formal a speech, makes a great one at the closing banquet.

He's in his glory and the authors are in the money.

Riding home in the pitcher's Caddy, Bob enjoys Johnny's insistence on selecting the Major Deegan to drive past Yankee Stadium, site of his greatest glory. But Bob shudders on the Thruway when, at seventy miles an hour, Podres keeps glancing at the tiny type of the Racing Form and tries to teach him how to understand it. They survive all the way, stopping along the highway for a Cinnabon, a Podres favorite, and reach a spaghetti dinner at Johnny's favorite Glens Falls Italian restaurant.

He buys.

The book tour fun continues. At Book Ends, a store on the main drag in Ridgewood, New Jersey, fans line up out the door and down the street to meet the pitcher, buy his book and get it signed. Weeks later, a second signing event take place there. Hall of Famer Cal Ripken Jr. has a book and major league baseball beat writer Maury Allen pitches his "Brooklyn Remembered" volume at the same time there too. That's the book his publisher chose over the Podres title but on this day, nobody cares about that (or Ripken's.)

The fans have come from the city, especially Brooklyn, plus Jersey, Connecticut and upstate New York and they only want to meet Podres and get his book. Allen and Ripken stare at each other while Bob and son Robert S. keep handing piles of copies for the pitcher to inscribe for adoring fans.

Among other venues are a book fair in Glens Falls at the Queensbury Hotel, site of Bob and the bride's wedding night. Upstate New Yorkers throng to the fair and all are Dodgers fans, including some who remember the pitcher from high school days in Witherbee and Mineville.

A bookstore in Cooperstown agrees to seat Bob and the pitcher on the sidewalk in front of the store on the main drag on Hall of Fame Day. They would sign books for the hordes of baseball nuts who throng to the town on this day. Bob drives down himself because his hero wants to drive himself. But Bob winds up signing and selling without him because he doesn't show up. Called that afternoon, Podres says he thought the gig was the next day, so he drives down then, without Bob, and signs and sells a pile of copies.

Copious reviewers praise the book. Papers in Brooklyn, Long Island, Cooperstown, Albany, Glens Falls, Burlington, Shelburne and Rutland are among them. Bob and Podres are interviewed on Burlington radio. Podres throws out the first pitch at a Lake Monsters minor league game in Burlington at Centennial Field, site of the first professional pitch Johnny ever threw. The Lake Monsters buy a hundred copies, which sell out immediately.

All the promotion, some of it engineered by Bob, ever a P.R. guy, and some by Heisman Trophy event director and other contacts in Brooklyn, leads to a 10,000-copy sellout of the first edition and another 10,000 of the second. Signed copies sell for $80 and more on eBay. At some bookstore venues several customers buy large numbers of signed copies that they put on eBay for auction.

John and son Bob hoard several signed copies that they think will increase in value. Some copies are sold to sports dinner organizers to be auctioned. The book becomes officially out of print after bringing profits to the authors and the pitcher. For Bob, who gambled with a self-published first edition and made money after all, the biggest reward by far is the time spent with his Dodgers hero. So there are no more fresh copies of the volume and at about the same time there is no more pitcher to sign them because Podres succumbs to a Glens Falls hospital leg surgery that stops his heart in 2008 at age seventy-six, fifty-three years after shutting out the Yankees.

Chapter Forty-three

The Best Full-Time Job

Who envisions a new career after retirement at age seventy? The bride attains that age when she becomes a full-time grandmother. A year later Bob leaves Bridge Building Images and believes he will do a lot of fishing. He has another think coming. Retirement brings revelations for both.

The new grandmother survives a second stroke only to snap her other hip. An ulcerated heel and nasal skin cancer surgery add suffering to the rheumatoid arthritis she has endured for years. Taken together, she needs Bob for everyday activity, from the time she wakes up. She swallows a handful of tablets and capsules twice a day, uses a walker, a cane, a stairlift. She needs visiting nurses, requires many physician appointments and physical therapy sessions. The upside for Bob includes admittance to the kitchen she kept as her private preserve for fifty something years and the chance to operate a washer and dryer. The most challenging part of the job: the bride dresses in style every day. Rather, Bob dresses her in style because she can't. It's the most challenging part of the day because he must display her drawers full of sweater sets or blouses and then hold up hanger after hanger of slacks for her approval.

Socks must match.

He cools his heels for excruciating minutes while she decides what to wear. Even so, he calls helping her his complete privilege. It also gives him time to ruminate.

Bob thinks he knows how the world works. Or at least the United States. He started out in the Empire State and the Garden State and the Golden State and the Green Mountain State but managed to visit all the others except Alaska. He would really like to fish for trout and salmon there, but the bride thinks the shopping might not be up to her standards, which are astronomical. If shopping were an Olympic event she would be on the middle podium, her head bent low from the weight around her neck of gold medals in boutique, mall, department store, discount, designer, chain, high-priced mom and pop and now even online. It's Bob's poor joke that Imelda Marcos phoned her to learn where she got her shoes.

As for his wardrobe, city and town, hill and dale, sophistication and hillbillyism, three-piece suits and Stein Bloch tuxes all felt appropriate in their time. Now he wears threadbare Viyella and Pendleton shirts and cheap jeans patched in the knees with duct tape. And sweatshirts, all cotton of course.

That is still the uniform for the best job of the man of the family,

One Acknowledgement

So many people helped me learn to write that I cannot possibly name them all. There is one, however, who gave me the kick in the pants I needed to start writing books.

One morning as I customarily read the New York Times on my commuter bus to New York, I was joined by Arnold Gingrich, founding editor of Esquire magazine, published for men with sartorial interests. I never would have guessed that was so because he had soup spots on his necktie, a frayed collar and a rumpled tweed jacket with elbow patches in need of new stitching. Arnold, who had published Ernest Hemingway, F. Scott Fitzgerald, William Faulkner and other famous writers, saw that I looked surprised at his appearance.

"The Saddle River runs through my property and I'm casting flies in it as many mornings as I can before I have to catch this bus. What do you want me to do when I'm fishing, wear a tux? Besides, nobody much comes to see me in the office."

Then he asked me what I did in the city. "You say you are a writer, so why are you reading the newspaper? You should use this time on the bus to write."

The next day I left the paper at home and got on the bus with a yellow pad.

Also by the author, (writing as Bob Bennett)

Rabbit Raising, merit badge manual (Boy Scouts of America)
Raising Rabbits the Modern Way (Garden Way Publishing)
Build Rabbit Housing (Garden Way Publishing)
The TFH Book of Pet Rabbits (TFH Publishing)
Rabbits as a Hobby (TFH Publishing)
Raising Rabbits Successfully (Williamson Publishing)
Bob Bennett's Guide to Winning Rabbit Shows (Dorn Publishing)
Storey's Guide to Raising Rabbits (Storey and Workman Publishing)
Rabbit Housing (Storey, Workman and Hachette Publishing)
Rabbit Management (section, Merck Veterinary Manual, Merck Inc.)
Johnny Podres, Brooklyn's Only Yankee Killer, with John and Robert S. Bennett (Rooftop Publishing)

CPSIA information can be obtained
at www.ICGtesting.com
Printed in the USA
JSHW060927271222
35404JS00002B/168